0   5   10   15   20   25
yards

The Zoo boundary when it first opened in 1931 — · — · —
Additional land with year of purchase — — — — —

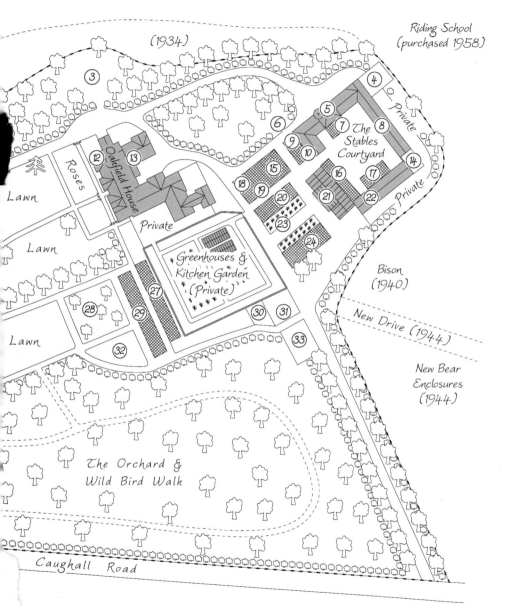

(1934)

Riding School
(purchased 1958)

③

④

⑤

⑥

⑦ The ⑧
Stables
Courtyard

⑨
⑩

⑫ Oakfield House ⑬

Roses

⑮

⑱
⑲

⑯

⑭

Private

Lawn

⑳

㉑

㉒

Private

Lawn

㉓

Private

㉔

Greenhouses &
Kitchen Garden
(Private)

Bison
(1940)

㉗

New Drive (1944)

㉘

㉙

㉚   ㉛

Lawn

㉜

㉝

New Bear
Enclosures
(1944)

The Orchard &
Wild Bird Walk

Caughall   Road

Chester Zoo in 1931

(Years of later developments shown in brackets)

1 – Llamas (1937)
2 – Peter & Lion (1942)
3 – Children's Play Area (1937)
4 – Indoor Lion Pen (1937)
5 – Original Lion Pen Archway
6 – Site for Outdoor Lion Enclosure
   (foundation stone laid 1937,
   building delayed until 1947)
7 – Griffon Vultures
8 – Mandrills & Leopards
9 – Penguins
10 – Tapir (1932)
11 – Malayan Bear (1937)
12 – Café
13 – Aquarium
14 – Elephants (1941)
15 – Bird Aviary
16 – Canadian Black Bears (Adam & Eve)
17 – Rhesus Monkeys
18 – Tourico Aviary
19 – Pelicans
20 – Pheasant Aviary
21 – Conservatory
   Crocodiles, Snakes, & Tropical Finches
22 – Chimps, Monkeys & Lemurs
23 – Herbaceous Borders
24 – Walk-through Aviary
25 – Parking
26 – Flamingos
27 – Bird Pens
28 – Small Orchard
29 – Aviary
30 – Coypu (1937)
31 – Polar Bear (1932)
32 – Porcupines
33 – Fallow Deer

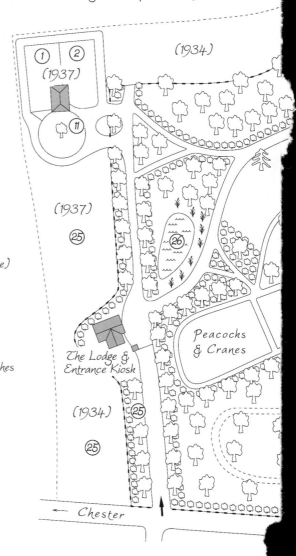

Riding School (purchased 1958)

(1934)

(1937)

The Lodge & Entrance Kiosk

Peacocks & Cranes

(1934)

← Chester

Map drawn by George Williams

Reared in Chester Zoo
The story of June Mottershead

Janice Madden

Map of Chester Zoo copyright © George Williams

Typeset - Ailsa Williams - BeeCOS - www.beecos.com

Cover Design by Consortium Design Ltd

ISBN 978-0-9559702-0-7

For

Elizabeth Atkinson Mottershead
who made all things possible

and

George, Muriel, Albert and Lucy Mottershead

also

The Staff who have loved and cared
for the animals over the last 75 years

ERECTED BY THE COUNCIL
OF THE
NORTH OF ENGLAND ZOOLOGICAL SOCIETY
IN MEMORY OF
ELIZABETH MOTTERSHEAD
1887-1969
WIFE OF THE FOUNDER OF
CHESTER ZOO
AS A TOKEN OF GRATITUDE
FOR HER 40 YEARS OF CONTINUOUS
EFFORT AND DEVOTION IN ESTABLISHING
THE ZOOLOGICAL GARDENS

Memorial plaque to the memory of
Elizabeth Mottershead
located near Oakfield House

'I am pushing my way through the tangled undergrowth, running along paths which lead me deeper and deeper into the garden.

I look up. The trees reach the sky. I shut my eyes. My shoes sink into the soft Cheshire soil. All around me are the sounds of small animals.

Where will the lions live? Will the elephants walk along these paths? Will the monkeys swing from these trees? Will we really live in the great red house? Will I live here forever?'

'This is my zoo.'

June Mottershead

Contents

1

'The Oakfield, the perfect place to start a zoo'

The small girl sat on the front step warmed by spring sunshine. Holding a twig with her right hand she traced out the word of the village where she lived: Shavington. It was a satisfying way of practising her letters whilst she kept an eye out for visitors. Then she thought hard about her newly learnt letters and carefully scratched out her full name: June Mottershead. Her big sister Muriel, known as Mew, would be pleased with her when she returned home from school.

Visitors would arrive soon, some of them walking from the centre of the village, to visit the small market garden attached to the rented house where the girl lived. She could hear children shouting and ran in quickly to call her mother out from the kitchen.

Soon she was wandering around the garden with her mother and the four visitors, listening to their comments about the aviaries, which held the finches and cranes. The boy and girl wandered off from their parents and she watched idly as the boy picked up a stone. She had seen all of this before and was well prepared for what would follow.

As he raised his hand to throw at the caged birds, she ran forward quickly and pushed him in the back. The stone fell to the ground and sulkily he returned to his mother's side, glaring at June. She smiled sweetly but even at four years of age she understood that when animals were not free, they were very much at the mercy of certain human beings.

It was nesting time and, as her mother pointed out, soon the aviaries would be expanded to accommodate newly purchased birds. In four weeks time a gibbon and a few rare marmosets would be housed in the cages that were presently half built.

The mother of the boy asked about buying a bird for her children. This was easily solved by taking a short trip into Crewe town, to Mill Street where June's parents had a florist shop. The produce from the market garden was sold

1

there directly to the public. June's father also had a number of small caged birds for sale.

The visitors knew of this particular shop as their neighbour had once rented it for the sale of baby linen. Next door to it was a milliner's. June felt proud of her mother as she quickly corrected the visitors. The Mottershead family now rented both shops, which were about to become one, for the florist business was expanding rapidly.

June returned to the front step, the family wandered off carrying the fresh vegetables that they had purchased during their stroll around the market garden and the boy stuck out his tongue at June. She ignored him, returning to her letters in the soil.

She missed Mew, her sister, even though she was ten years older than the little girl. Already she helped out at the expanding Mill Street shop, every spare moment being taken up by the business. Together with her father, George Mottershead, generally known as Mr Mott, she ran the Crewe shop every Saturday. June also had her own small jobs to attend to and soon she would be helping to feed the birds. Standing by her mother's side she listened as the small birds responded to that gentle reassuring voice. They tilted their tiny heads to one side, reacting to her calm words. June slid her arms around her mother's skirt, feeling happy and loved. Elizabeth Mottershead, known as Lizzie, always cared for all the animals and spoke to every one no matter how tired she felt.

They moved on to the goats, two of which were about to have kids. Her mother gently slid her hands over their expanding bellies, touching them softly and pointing out to June the spasmodic movement of the babies.

Next came the boarding kennels where three dogs were housed during the absence of their owners. Finally they checked on a number of strays that had been given to the Mottershead family by the local people who had soon become appreciatively aware of their caring ways towards unfortunate animals.

June fed the orphaned cats and the one stray dog. Her father had already cautioned her not to become too friendly with the old terrier but the little girl scooped him up and held him tightly to her chest. Her mother smiled down at her, understanding her love for neglected creatures.

"Now, June, remember what your father said. No more sneaking him into the house."

"Mum, tell me again about when you were a little girl. The bit about caring for the baby lambs when their mothers died and the bit about the snow and the ..."

"Stop!" laughed Lizzie. "We'd be at it all day! But tonight when I tuck you up in bed I will tell you more about the sheep farm, though goodness knows you've heard it all about a hundred times. Right now I have to finish cooking dinner for all of you. Grandad has worked hard in the garden all day; without him we would have no produce to sell in our shop.

With that she hurried inside to continue her chores but June knew that she always fed the animals and birds before concentrating on family meals.

That night over dinner there was much talk about the business, the impending arrival of the gibbon and the other monkeys and the possibility and cost of turning the tiny menagerie into a zoo.

June sat next to Mew but neither of them spoke. These were important matters, which affected all of them, though they were included in the discussion as listeners only.

"But George, can we afford it?" Her mother looked concerned.

"More and more visitors are coming here to Shavington. Several of them say that if this little 'zoo', for want of a better word, expands they would be willing to pay an entrance fee. It is growing fast Lizzie, and we could pay someone to help. We haven't got time to do that as you have the animals to look after and I am running the shop. Soon we will be receiving visitors instead of sightseers and we will have to turn them away.

"Today a man called in at the shop. He is one of the founders of the Crosville Motor Company. He proposed that we open as a small zoo to the public and Crosville would then run a special service from Crewe to Shavington each weekend. Visitors would love a day out to Shavington. What do you think?"

"But can we afford to make the changes, buy more animals?" his wife persisted.

"I think we need to take in a business partner. Dr English is interested in putting in some money and working with us. We get along well. I think this would be a possibility."

June felt very sleepy but pinched herself awake. All of this meant big changes. She didn't understand a lot of it but if it meant a zoo, a real zoo, then it had to be good.

Soon she was tucked up in bed. Her mother sat by her side telling her about life as a small girl, a hard life on a sheep farm in Westmorland where the animals came first and the winters were treacherous. Again and again June insisted on the twin lamb story she had heard many times before, until she finally fell asleep, her head buzzing with thoughts of cages containing all kinds of animals, even those she'd only heard of in the Noah's Ark story.

From then on everything seemed to happen at once. The cages were completed and occupied by the lively gibbon and several monkeys. Her father had placed branches inside so that the monkeys could swing to and fro, much to the amusement of the ever-expanding number of now paying visitors.

During the summer evenings the two sisters were allowed to bring the gibbon from his cage and he played with them, extending his long arms around June's neck. It was a relief to the family when the zoo closed in the evening and they began to check both the animals and cages, repetitious but necessary work which would grow alongside the needs of the zoo.

Bears, reptiles and exotic birds were added to the collection and space for them began to diminish. June watched her father many times as he endeavoured to build larger cages in which to give the animals some limited freedom.

From the North and Midlands people came in their hundreds, in cars and by the local bus service. Often they would repeat their visits as news of additional animals to the zoo spread. There were other callers too, unemployed men who were desperate for food in return for odd jobs. Mrs Mottershead was very upset, as she could not help them; it was a hard time for everyone as the Depression bit deeper into their lives.

Talk at meal times consisted of the immediate success of the little zoo, the frustration of not providing more open space and, above all, lack of room for expansion. Finding more money was a huge problem for the Mottershead family.

June knew from snippets of conversation that there had been a disagreement with Mr English on how to develop the zoo, so it came as no surprise to hear that they would leave Shavington.

In September 1930 her mother told her that a move was imminent.

"Where to, Mum?" was her immediate response for she had been aware of the atmosphere of potential change for some time. Muriel would soon finish at the convent school and was already preparing to work in the family business; her matter-of-fact approach had reassured June. Everyone seemingly had backed her father in his search for a home for the family and a place to start another zoo.

Lizzie explained the situation to her small daughter. Finally her father had discovered a small estate near to Chester in the village of Upton. The Depression had sent property values tumbling and Mr Mott's search had led him to seven acres of lawns, gardens, shrubberies and orchards.

A large, red brick Victorian mansion named The Oakfield provided living quarters while outbuildings, a striking black and white lodge, a spacious courtyard, a walled kitchen garden and a conservatory were also part of the estate. £3,500 was the asking price and could be raised by a mortgage.

Two weeks before the final negotiations were done June's father reassured the entire family that this was the perfect place to start a zoo. There would be no small cages, no bars, and no walls. June imagined all the animals wandering around quite freely but later Mew explained that this would not be the case. Some of the animals might be allowed to wander and others, although contained, would not be placed behind bars. Her father had plans and dreams because, until then, no zoo in Britain had been built in this way.

Mr English would continue to run the Shavington enterprise. June's little world of Shavington and the surrounding Cheshire villages went all topsy-turvy within weeks as they moved out from their home. Together with her mother and sister she stayed in lodgings for two months, October and November, in Mill Street, Crewe until early December. It was a miserable time as she missed the small zoo but she knew that soon they would be moving to a big house near to Chester. She looked round at the grey, windswept streets of Crewe and walked past the shop in Mill Street with her sister, knowing that it was no longer theirs. However, her mother was cheerful and showed no doubts about the momentous move, so why should she?

June's father was called away a few days before the move. He had been offered a pair of black bears, the corporation of Matlock, Derbyshire asking him if he wanted them for the new zoo. As they were leaving behind all their animals at Shavington, these Canadian black bears would be much appreciated at the new location.

But right now the rest of the Mottershead family were more concerned with the move to their new home. Lizzie and her two daughters waited until Mew finished school at the Convent and on December the seventh they prepared to leave Crewe in a pantechnicon that was crammed full – with furniture, a gibbon and two goats.

"I want to sit in the back with the animals," June begged, but she was firmly placed on her mother's knee in the front and her sister had the enviable job of travelling with the small representation of the Shavington Zoo.

They drove along winter roads but as dusk came, icy rain began to fall. The van took the wrong turning and ended up in a narrow country lane. Her mother grew weary and stopped singing to her so June began to excitedly imagine her new home.

No one was there to meet them as they drove onto the estate, the headlights providing only quick glimpses of an enormous red building. Mr Mott was busy capturing the bears at Matlock and there were no welcoming lights for Lizzie and her two daughters.

They clambered out of the van, relieved to move at last, their feet mulching the soggy remains of autumn leaves. They then began the difficult job of lifting the furniture from the van into the hall of the huge building. June looked up as she stood on the sodden drive but the headlights from the vehicle only lit up the bottom half of the old mansion. She shivered, wondering what adventures lay ahead.

Trying to be of help, and hearing her tired mother sigh, she carried small objects into the house, then the equally exhausted gibbon, finally returning for the goats. For this night, at least, everything and everyone must stay in the house until morning.

Elizabeth came well prepared with a number of candles, which were lit and carefully carried up the steps. Each one flickered a dismal welcome as it dripped wax onto the floor where it had been placed, casting alarming shadows up the walls.

Imposing doors opened to reveal by candlelight the black and white marble floor, oak doors leading off from each side and, beyond, the wooden staircase mounting to the bedrooms. The candlelight only lit up small flickering pools in the mansion, giving just sufficient light by which to bring in the furniture.

It was all very frightening for June but the thing that shocked her most was the penetrating cold that filled her lungs. The air was still and icy, even worse than out on the grass where at least the wind blew. This cold seemed almost visible, wrapping itself around each one of them so that conversation ceased and the only sounds came from the chattering Woolly Monkey and the bleating of the goats.

The electricity was not turned on, nor was the water, and of course there was no telephone. It felt as if they were cut off from everything in the outside world. June sat huddled up on a stool, cuddling the gibbon, whilst the driver, her mother and sister struggled to climb the stairs with the brass bedstead. Finally the big feather mattress was placed on it and they at least had a warm bed in which to rest.

Keeping their clothes on for warmth, Lizzie and her two daughters snuggled down into the deep, feathery expanse, falling into an exhausted sleep.

June was awake first in the morning. Very quietly she slid out of bed to explore the house. The air was musty as she wandered down the stone steps towards the servants' quarters. Amazed, she saw what appeared to be snow, at least an inch deep, covering the red floor tiles. Very carefully she touched the white stuff with her foot. It broke up, tiny pieces floating into the sunbeams that slanted through the windows. It wasn't snow at all, it was mould!

Stifling a giggle, she approached the garden door and struggled to open it. She gasped with delight for the view in front of her was magical. Great cedars skirted an extensive lawn and beyond lay Victorian shrubberies of laurels, rhododendrons and variegated hollies. Winter sunshine stippled the garden and squirrels skirmished on the grass in front of her.

Rotting brown leaves from autumn lay thickly on the lawn and covered every path. In amazement she sat down on the steps that led from The Oakfield, arcing her small body backwards to stare up at the red building. She gasped, for it was enormous. Window after uncurtained window looked down on her until she felt that she was being watched. Her bottom was cold so she clambered up to jump down the steps, landing with a thud on the thick brown leaves. She slipped down with a bump, feeling the wet earth seep instantly through her thin clothes.

"Serves you right for sneaking off without me," laughed Mew, her smile sweet and reassuring. "Mum sent me to look for you. Come on, let's explore together."

Together they set off, hand-in-hand, to ramble across their seven acres of neglected gardens and orchards.

George Mottershead -
outside his shop in Mill Street Crewe

The Oakfield Zoological Gardens Shavington

Muriel and June at Shavington Zoo

2

'The entire day seemed like one great adventure'

June loved her big sister; already she seemed like a woman. Schooling at the convent had finished only the day before her fourteenth birthday, but there had been no birthday celebrations.

The grounds of The Oakfield lay hushed in winter sleep. The mystery surrounding their overgrown paths and the wilderness that had once been gardens silenced the two girls as they explored the orchards, the walled kitchen garden, the bare conservatory and the courtyard with all its strange empty buildings. Soon the damp from the rotting debris of autumn soaked their thin shoes and chilled them. The winter sunshine filtered through the webbed, naked branches, and June shivered.

At any moment she expected to see a castle and a sleeping princess like the one in her storybook. She pulled at Mew's hand and the girls stopped, surrounded by the twigs and branches. Beneath their feet lay the fruits of the horse chestnut trees, conkers partly spilled from their cases but cracked and rotting. Their feet trod on layer upon layer of leaf mould, which June kicked into, releasing the musty smell of disintegration.

Everything was returning to the earth to be stored as in a giant squirrel's nest, ready for spring. There was such stillness, a hush, that the girls found themselves whispering to each other, their breath rising in spirals as the iciness penetrated their lungs.

"What will happen, Mew? Where will the zoo be?"

Mew knelt down, hugging her sister.

"It will happen June, don't you worry. Dad will make it happen. He has already described to me how it will be. It will be a zoo without bars. A zoo surrounded by beautiful gardens. And we will live in the big red house. Grandfather and grandmother will live in the black and white lodge nearby. It was too dark to see everything last night but our grandparents will arrive today."

"But the animals – will they wander about in this?" She looked round hopelessly.

"Of course not," Her sister spoke softly. "They will not live in cages and look out from behind bars but they won't wander freely all over the place either. Be patient June. Just wait and see."

Far away they heard their mother calling them back and the exploration was over. Retracing their steps along the broken pathways, they were at last facing the great red mansion. Smoke was spiralling from one of the chimneys, their mother stood on the top step waving to them and June was amazed to notice for the first time the thick Pyracantha creeper which covered the front of the house. Tunnels of leaves grew up to encase each window; green columns which blanketed the red brickwork, reaching as high as the guttering.

Releasing her sister's hand, she raced across the lawns to where the goats were already tethered.

"Your grandparents have arrived. Grandad is already brushing up the leaves so it is work, work, work for all of us now."

"But breakfast first," and her mother and sister followed her into the kitchen which was now mercifully free of mould.

The entire day seemed like one great adventure, carrying, sweeping, calling out over new discoveries, and helping her grandmother in the lodge, the black and white building nearby festooned in thick variegated ivy. Finally June curled up on the window seat which looked out over the cedars, the shrubberies and lawns, contented and satisfied with the stew that her mother had managed to produce in the grand kitchen at the back of the mansion.

Away from the kitchen range, June quickly felt the winter cold begin to wrap its cold fingers around her, but she was loath to join the others round the table, resolving instead to watch for any foxes which might cross the lawns in the dusk of the icy winter evening.

Pulling her thin knees up tight to her body, she made herself as small as possible, a scrap of a girl about to embark on a new life of adventure and excitement. Caught up in her father's ambitious dream and her mother's devotion and love, her sister's determination and her grandparents' total support, there were no doubts in her mind. It would all happen because her father said so and there was no question about it.

Shavington already seemed such a very long way away.

Long shadows spilled across the lawns, imperceptibly melting into each other and growing into solid darkness. A full moon lit up the branches of the cedars and stealthily a dog fox crossed the grass, padding an ancient path trodden by generations of his kind.

June blinked and he was gone, his red coat no longer visible. She turned to say something then changed her mind. The fox would be her secret but over the years she would see him many times, and twice a vixen with her sharp eyed cubs.

For many decades fox hunting had taken place over the estate, the hounds baying and the meet gathering in the winter months at the foot of the mansion steps. For the next few months the Mottershead family seemed merely the visitors on this estate until they established the pattern of their lives. Life in the mansions of England had continued down the generations, nothing being disturbed or changed for years. It would take time to change a gentleman's residence, even that of a very wealthy middle class gentleman, into a zoo.

The Oakfield had been one of the first of the smaller estates of Upton to be sold off for urban development. During the late Victorian years many Liverpool cotton and tea merchants had bought up rich farming land on which to build their own private mansions. With them they brought huge financial wealth, which influenced local authorities.They were the new affluent of Britain, looked down upon by the aristocracy who existed through generations of their bloodline. These wealthy merchants were respected because they had brought jobs and prosperity to the towns and villages of a country in the clutches of the Depression. They had the power of the vote on the councils and the unspoken influence of wealth within the rural communities.

Rumblings, rumours, and dissent were already muttering their way through the local council members within the area of Chester. A zoo was not something that the respectable citizens of Upton would necessarily want.

The little girl knew none of this. She sat at the gateway of her future, entranced and apprehensive but secure in the credibility and integrity of her father's passionate vision.

Later, much later, her father scooped her up from the window seat and carried her to bed. In the dark the headlights of his van had lit up the driveway as he returned from the long drive from Matlock, stopping briefly at Crewe. With him he brought the two large black bears, Adam and Eve, finally released from their dreadful place of captivity, a foul smelling cave in the Derbyshire hills.

Before entering The Oakfield, he and his friend who had assisted him in the capture of the bears, drove into the courtyard behind the big house. Calmed by the movement of the truck, the two animals quietly entered the converted and iron-lined horsebox that had been prepared for them. Once they were bedded down for the night, Mr Mott was finally able to join his family and talk went on far into the night.

The family heard about the horrendous problem of extricating the two bears from a cave where they had been kept. It was barred but visitors could look in at the captives. Both had grown so large that they could hardly stand up and visitors no longer wished to see them. The female bear was captured and crated very quickly but the mistrusting and troubled male resisted any attempts and refused to come out of the cave. It took three days and nights of hard work to secure him, but these bears became the first new arrivals at the new zoo.

Excited by the success of the bears' capture and the final journey to the estate, Mr Mott discussed the future of the zoo. Money would be very tight, for all their savings had gone towards the purchase or had been set aside for its immediate upkeep. His parents' life savings and every last penny of his own money and his wife's savings had now gone.

Their actual immediate income would be the ten shillings a week pension paid to his parents but they relied on the mercy of the bank if they became desperate for finance. The loan had had to be negotiated through a private mortgage, as no bank would support the venture.

Much discussion took place on that first night. The animals would occupy the stables in the courtyard, and any reptiles they might collect could happily exist among the plants in the conservatory. Pheasants, peacocks and ornamental doves could roam about the estate freely but aviaries would be built for birds of prey, parrots and tropical finches.

No one would be paid a salary.

The following day Mr Mott went to the local shop to buy a newspaper. His youngest daughter June accompanied him and he read aloud the delightful report on the capture of the two bears at Matlock.

"Eve falls for the apple but Adam won't bite," was the headline, causing him to laugh loudly.

"This will be good publicity for our zoo," he told June, proceeding to tell her once again about the capture of the two bears from their awful prison cave.

On the walk back to the zoo he met an old man who lived at Upton. During their conversation the man told him that he was sad to hear of all the trouble.

"Don't worry about that lot," smiled Mr Mott. "The bears are safely rescued and are here now with us."

"No, I don't mean that," the old man hastened to explain. "A petition has started in the village to stop you opening the zoo. They don't like the idea of it at all, all those dangerous, smelly animals that might escape, and all the fairground stuff that could start up. Things like roundabouts and all kinds of things. The petition has spread to Chester now."

June ran alongside her father as he hastened to break the news to the family. Then he caught the bus into town to see his bank manager. Confirmation of the rumour was needed. Surely it couldn't be true. After all, it was the last thing he wanted. Fripperies like fairgrounds were no part of his dream for the zoo without bars and he certainly wouldn't be enclosing the property within a ten-foot wall.

June sat on the steps waiting for her father's return. One look at his expression told her that the rumours were true. She continued to sit on the step whilst her father hurried inside to share the awful news.

Later, when she was in the kitchen standing on a footstool to help her mother wash up, she began to ask questions.

"What is an enquiry, Mum? What does it mean?"

"Your father will fight all of this, June. He says we will have our zoo. In order to do this there is to be a public enquiry, which means someone will come to the zoo and find out exactly what we are doing and why we are doing it. It is finding out about the truth, June, and believe me the truth is a very strong thing. Don't you worry your little head about any of this! Try and do little jobs and help Mew with the animals."

But June could see that her mother was sad and worried.

Over the next few months The Oakfield property changed into an ordered estate. Rambling roses were tamed, trees pruned, leaves scraped from the paths, brambles cut back and grass trimmed.

June's grandfather worked as hard as any man half his age, only stopping for lunch. He would go up to the lodge where granny had cooked him a meal, allowing himself half an hour's snooze afterwards before returning to work. He smiled at June, showing her the new growth on the plants and trees. She stared in wonder at his large, veined hands as they worked miracles on the regrowth. Maybe the plants were rewarding him by their sap rising quickly to produce the first green buds of spring, the first spring in their new home. He worked from dawn to dusk, a reassuring figure, bent over the foliage, his thick white beard and flat cap betraying his presence as he was often almost perfectly camouflaged in the shrubbery.

"Cut everything back sharp, June," he would say, his eyes twinkling when he offered her the secateurs for a little while. And so she learnt about living things under the guidance of her grandfather whose determination often reminded her of her father.

Her rather prim grandmother was not enamoured of the zoo animals and nature in general, and so helped in other ways. She concentrated on the two homes and showed great skill in making 'a little go a long way'.

Mew explained to her sister that their grandparents could manage 'on an oily rag', whatever that meant. Albert and Lucy had experienced the effects of the First World War and the Depression, known very hard times and well understood the expression 'tightening their belts'.

June never heard either of them complain.

June's mother worked relentlessly from sun-up to sunset, often falling into an exhausted sleep by the fire after the evening meal. She turned the morning room of The Oakfield into a café, cooked for everyone, supervised Mew, organised unpaid helpers and friends and checked on all the animals. She also fed everyone who helped as a way of thanking them, for there was no money and no one knew if the zoo could open until the court case was over.

Mew had become the first zookeeper. She cleaned out the cages every day, fed the animals and gave them fresh drinking water. June took it all in as she trailed after her along the now tidy pathways, watching carefully as she fed and watered each creature. Copying her mother, she also talked to them and noted their condition daily.

Other helpers arrived on the estate, more unpaid friends and relations of both her mother and her father. Together they began to build pens and enclosures following the guidelines of Mr Mott who was squaring up to fight an expensive court case to make it possible to open the zoo.

Eve Falls For The Apple.

News Chronicle
Dec 3/30

ADAM WON'T BITE.

From Our Own Correspondent.

MATLOCK, Tuesday.

Apples have proved to be the undoing of Eve, the rebellent black bear who refused to leave her cage here, yesterday, when it was sought to transfer her to her new home.

Adam, her companion, refused to be tempted and still defies his would-be captors.

The two animals have spent the summer and autumn in "Rovers' Walk" here, and were recently sold to Mr. G. S. Mottershead, of Mill-street, Crewe, the new owner of the Oakfield Estate, Chester, where he is opening a zoo.

Apples, cabbage, bread and honey were handed down in a trap cage to the bear, but it was over an hour before Eve got into the trap and was caught.

Eve has the strength of an elephant, and began to burst the wooden partitions of the cage and bend the iron bars.

Mr. Mottershead and his assistant feared Eve would burst the cage and go to the woods which surround the menagerie.

The services were secured of a blacksmith who produced iron bars to add to the strength of the cage, but even these Eve bent with her enormous strength.

Finally, Mr. Mottershead had to add more iron work, which he hoped would enable him to take Eve safely to her new home at Chester.

Adam is to be tackled again later.

The Cheshire Hunt crossing in front of The Oakfield, 1931.

June and Adam the Canadian black bear

Grandad Mottershead

3

'The Court Case'

The proposal for a zoo at Upton met with fierce opposition. George Mottershead made it clear that he wished to use the property for the purposes of a zoological garden and aviary but once the proposal was put forward, the petitions began and huge opposition grew. A petition was presented to the council with between 600 and 700 locals objecting. Many residents of Upton drew lurid pictures of incidents which might occur if a zoo was established near to their village.

Opposition towards the zoo grew. The Chester Rural District Council and the Chester Town Planning Committee refused to consider the proposal even though it was pointed out that Mr Mottershead had for many years run a successful zoo at Shavington, near Crewe. All information fell on deaf ears. Such an idea would not be tolerated.

George Mottershead, however, had a dream of a ground-breaking zoo without bars and his passion for the ideas he had brought with him from Shavington made him determined to fight the decision. Land near to The Oakfield was already being sold for housing and he knew that the legal proposal for the zoo presented on his behalf needed to be handled in a highly professional manner. He sought the strongest representation through a legal expert.

He hired a barrister, Mr Hugh Gamon, of Whitley and Bevan, who opened the case for him at the Town Hall in Chester on February the sixth 1931. It was an enormous and expensive decision to hire a lawyer to present the case. The Mottershead family waited, sensing the tension in Mr Mottershead. They desperately wanted a successful outcome from the court case, yet knew that this could be the end of all their plans.

The Oakfield and its seven acres was prime Cheshire land, near to the picturesque village of Upton. Opening the case for Mr Mottershead, Mr Gamon pointed out that the house and land had been purchased by Mr Mottershead who believed that no restrictions had been placed on its use. When he entered into the contract Mr Mottershead was informed that his enterprise came within the Town

Planning Scheme.

It was only at that point that he became aware of the mounting opposition towards his plans for a zoo. His belief was that the residents of Upton would thoroughly endorse the scheme. The Oakfield was a large house and, like many others of its kind, it had been difficult to find buyers who would use it as a home.

The Oakfield was very self-contained, hidden away by trees and shrubberies. It was intended to use the house as a residence and the gardens as an aviary and zoological gardens but there had been a misinterpretation as to the meaning of 'zoological gardens'. Residents thought that tigers and lions would wander there. In fact the only occupants, and they were caged, were two black bears which he had been told were as tame as Alsatian dogs. Replying to the Inspector of Health, he pointed out that there were no animals to make noises such as howling wolves and roaring lions.

Mr Mottershead then spoke up. Introduced as a Fellow of the Zoological Society, London, he explained that he had lived in Crewe for eleven years, and several years before had established an aviary and zoological gardens within a residential area of Shavington. He had withdrawn from this small zoo in 1930, proposing to keep birds and small animals such as monkeys and porcupines in larger premises. He already kept two black 'teddy' bears, known as Canadian black bears, as pets.

At Shavington, where at least nine men were employed and refreshments were available to visitors, many people came by private cars and large numbers of school children attended for natural history lessons. Special terms existed for teachers in order to facilitate this.

He described to the interested listeners how he had been born among animals. His father was a great botanist working with orchids. When the orchids arrived from abroad, packed in wooden cases, the contents also revealed small reptiles, which he used to collect and keep. His interest in animals grew.

He went on to explain the importance of the sewerage system at The Oakfield. It was in an area which was drained under the Chester Corporation scheme. The previous owner had had an arrangement with the Corporation of Chester, permitting him to connect the buildings belonging to The Oakfield to the sewer.

There was no official agreement, though, to say that the owner of The Oakfield had a right to join those buildings to the sewer that connected with the Corporation sewer. If the Corporation discontinued that agreement it would become virtually impossible to occupy either the house or grounds of The Oakfield unless an expensive sewerage plant was installed.

The Corporation had indicated to the Rural Council that unless an agreement had been reached, they would discontinue the agreement. The Rural Council had received no indication that the Corporation would take and treat anything other than domestic matter.

There was a muttering in the courtroom at this and several satisfied smiles.

Mr Gamon spoke, addressing himself to Mr H. G. Williams, representing Chester Rural District Council. "Do I understand by this, Mr Williams, that Council would refuse us permission to have a cess-pool? Would they refuse any farmer who was not connected with the main drains such permission?"

Mr Williams: "I do not think so."

Mr Gamon: "I suggest not."

In reply to Mr Ouseley Smith, the solicitor representing the residents of Upton, Mr Mottershead said that he had no objection to telling the court what he had paid for the property. The amount was £3,500. He believed the rates to be about £17 for half a year, heating and lighting would be about £90 a year and wages would be around £20 a week. Feeding would be around £100 a year.

Mr Smith: "What would the total amount be?"

Mr Mottershead: "About £2000 a year."

Mr Smith: "And you expect about a hundred visitors a week?"

Mr Mottershead: "That would not include season ticket holders. Also, we may make more money if we have surplus stock."

Mr Smith: "But you never referred to selling being your chief object in your proposal?"

At this Mr Mottershead frowned slightly. "It is not. If we get a successful specimen we sell it."

"So, on your reckoning your income would not be more than £780 and you have to make £1,220 more to make a profit?"

Mr Mottershead remained calm and focused. "You have not reckoned up the season ticket holders."

"I put it to you that you will have to make nearly twice as much as you would make from the 'gate'. You intend to draw large crowds of people and if you do not, you will not be successful."

"It depends what you mean by 'large crowds'. I do not consider one hundred people a day to be a large number."

"I suggest that you are misleading the Inspector."

"I cannot say as to numbers."

Mr Smith looked irritated. He sighed before speaking. "Are you going to make it pay, or are you a philanthropic institution?"

"I want to make it pay."

"What was your past occupation?"

"I was a naturalist and a nurseryman."

"Do you think there will be any interference with the amenities at Upton?"

"None whatsoever."

The Town Clerk then cross-examined Mr Mottershead at some length. Having heard Mr Mottershead say that he did not intend to put up any additional buildings, the Town Clerk then addressed him directly.

"Don't you think you will attract people in large numbers?"

"People will come in large numbers, but not too large."

"What is to prevent them? How would you prevent them coming in large numbers?"

"If people came in hundreds and thousands," he replied, "I would raise the entrance fee."

Laughter rippled through the courtroom and George Mottershead tried to hide a smile.

"Once you had started with this zoo, would you add other attractions, which would detract from the value of property in this village? Would it not be far better for the house to be occupied as a residence?"

Mr Mottershead drew a deep breath. "No. The property would be better occupied for the purposes I propose than remaining empty and no rates being paid on it."

Mr Mottershead then went on to make an emphatic denial. He would not be misusing the house and grounds. Upton had existed as a village for centuries and was made up of old world cottages and larger houses. It was free from industrial disturbance. The Oakfield was a beautiful house, superbly built and designed and it was absurd to say that it had lost its value as a residence.

These were times of economic distress and at present houses the size of The Oakfield were not selling. This would not last. The project might be a huge success and bring thousands of people to the area. If it failed, he would be the only one affected. In no way did it devalue the cost of surrounding property.

He then pointed out that it was desirable for Chester to have a zoo. All cities should have one, from an educational point of view. It was far better for children to see live animals in their natural state than dead and stuffed in their skins.

He referred to the many incorrect articles in a number of newspapers which had been handed in to the court. These articles suggested that the rateable value of the surrounding properties would be lowered.

"I quote from one of the articles: 'I think they are having more than zoological gardens. They are going to have a dirt track, electric hare racing and a dance hall'."

Mr Mottershead then addressed the court, speaking quietly but firmly.

"I selected The Oakfield because it was in the centre of an agricultural district and I did not want to be near municipal works, or too close to a main road because it was essential that I have peace and quietness at my establishment for breeding purposes.

"I considered buying Backford Hall as a place for the zoo but turned it down as it was too near to the main road. A site in Sealand Road did not answer my purpose because of the football ground which attracted too many people and the noise made by them might startle foreign birds, especially at breeding times. "

He explained to the Court why the houses close to the proposed zoo would not be affected. His explanation to one owner, Mr Paterson, produced a positive reaction to the proposed idea. The second house owner, Mr Beresford Jones, had said there would be no opposition to the idea.

At this, Mr Beresford Jones sprang to his feet immediately to protest. "I deny that absolutely!" he cried out.

This emphatic denial of support for the zoo ominously closed the morning session, the enquiry adjourning for lunch.

Colonel Brown, an estate agent, began the afternoon session, notifying the Court of the arterial road at Upton which would be divided into two parts, the northern and the southern. The southern part included houses like The Lawns, owned by Sir John Frost, and the northern part contained cottages and small suburban houses.

Visitors to The Oakfield would go from Chester via Newton or past Upton Mill, and traffic and people coming from Liverpool and Birkenhead to The Oakfield would use the new road. The building of the arterial road would cause so much disturbance when it was cut out that The Oakfield proposition in comparison would be a mere nothing.

Replying to a question from the barrister, Mr Gamon, Colonel Brown said that he had heard that Chester Corporation was considering an aerodrome in the neighbourhood. He added that as a member of Chester Natural Science Society he thought that the Zoological Garden would be a considerable facility to the Zoological section of the Society.

Mr Gamon: "Speaking as a citizen, would you say that Chester is a little deficient as regards walks?"

Col. Brown: "Yes. There are few walks except the Meadows or in the Upton direction."

Mr H. G. Williams: "As an estate agent, if you had the whole of Upton in your hands for sale, would you consider it advantageous to have the place there?"

Col. Brown: "In view of the sort of property it is and in view of the houses being put up in Upton now, I think it would be desirable."

Mr Williams: "Do you think Chester would be benefited by the attraction of The Oakfield?"

Col. Brown: "Oh, I don't think you could expect a very large number of people coming to Chester because of The Oakfield."

Mr Williams: "If an Assessment Committee formed the opinion that there was an injurious effect caused by development, then their proper cause would be to reduce the assessment of properties round about?"

Col. Brown: "Yes."

Colonel Brown, replying to Mr Smith in regard to the building of the arterial road, said the road would reduce amenities from the point of view of the purposes for which it had been set aside under the Town Planning Scheme. If the arterial road and the Aerodrome were to go through, the Zoological Gardens would be a very small matter.

Mr Williams: "Would it not be better to wait until the greater projects are carried out before carrying out that of The Oakfield?"

Col. Brown: "My answer to that is 'No!' because, as I have said, I don't think that The Oakfield project would be detrimental."

Colonel Brown agreed with the Town Clerk that the present roads, Sandpit Street and Smoke Street, in Upton, were not suitable for the current traffic.

Mr John Lightfoot of Upton and Mr W. Eaton of Shavington gave evidence in favour of the appeal and the Town Clerk then opened the case for the Chester Corporation Town Planning Committee.

The Town Clerk: "Upton is the best residential neighbourhood in the immediate proximity of Chester?"

Col. Brown: "I should think it is the only village that could be described as a residential village."

Mr Hugh Gamon then re-examined the cost of The Oakfield: "The cost of this house to Mr Mottershead was £3,500. That does not represent the value of the bricks and mortar, or the money spent on it?"

Col. Brown: "No, not at all."

John Lightfoot, a grocer in Chester, spoke in favour of the appeal. As a resident he would welcome a zoological gardens there. He admitted that he had bought birds from Mr Mottershead.

The chairman of the improvement committee said the opinion of the Town Planning Authority was that The Oakfield was not a suitable place for a zoological gardens and aviary.

Mr Williams, addressing the Inspector on behalf of the Rural District Council, said that they opposed the application on the grounds that the premises ought not to be used for a zoo. Upton was an exclusive area and a zoological gardens in its midst was not a suitable or proper development.

The chairman of the Chester Rural District Council said that in his opinion there were more suitable areas outside Upton for such a purpose.

Mr Smith, who appeared on behalf of the residents of Upton to oppose the scheme, said that if the application were granted many people would come to the village. Amenities would be affected and the zoo would introduce 'people of mixed types'. These undesirable people would end their visit to the zoo by proceeding to the local public house or any place where a village dance was in progress. No one could visualize what might happen as a result.

It would be a terrible thing to allow any newcomers to enter the parish and destroy the character of the place simply to gratify commercial desires and ambitions. That was why planning schemes were put into place.

Mr Beresford Jones, whose property was near to The Oakfield, said the zoo would have a detrimental affect on his property. It was totally untrue that he had supported the idea of a zoo. From the first moment he had opposed it. He conceded that Mr Mottershead had said in an interview that a zoo was preferable to a lot of small houses being erected on the site. Also, great crowds of people in the village would destroy the residential character of Upton.

The president of the Upton Women's Institute, the chairman of Upton Parish Council and the building surveyor to Chester Rural Council also gave evidence against the application.

Mr Gamon, in his closing address, said it was absurd to call the Zoological Gardens an industrial development. If someone had wanted to turn The Oakfield into a boys' or girls' school there would have been no objection. Mr Mottershead said that he had not been given the opportunity to explain his scheme. The Town Planning Committee turned it down before getting the full details and before hearing what Mr Mottershead had to present. That was in great defiance of the circular received from the Ministry, and not a matter of common justice. The man had bought the property for £3,500 and it was not fair to prevent him using it in the way he wanted without giving him the opportunity to state his case.

The opposition's case rested on the desire to keep people from Upton. This was an impossible attitude in this day with regard to a village so near to Chester. Chester was a city of which everyone was proud. People were invited to visit and trade was good. Yet, only two miles out of Chester did they not want people? It was selfish and old fashioned and, as such, in keeping with the 'old world' attitude of Upton.

Mr Gamon and the Town Clerk thanked the Inspector of Health. The Inspector announced to the court that he would visit The Oakfield the next day and anyone who wished to accompany him was welcome to do so.

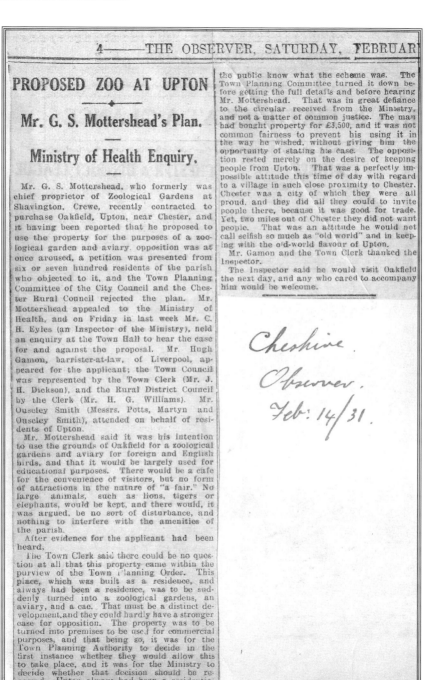

4——THE OBSERVER, SATURDAY, FEBRUARY

PROPOSED ZOO AT UPTON

Mr. G. S. Mottershead's Plan.

Ministry of Health Enquiry.

Mr. G. S. Mottershead, who formerly was chief proprietor of Zoological Gardens at Shavington, Crewe, recently contracted to purchase Oakfield, Upton, near Chester, and it having been reported that he proposed to use the property for the purposes of a zoological garden and aviary, opposition was at once aroused, a petition was presented from six or seven hundred residents of the parish who objected to it, and the Town Planning Committee of the City Council and the Chester Rural Council rejected the plan. Mr. Mottershead appealed to the Ministry of Health, and on Friday in last week Mr. C. H. Eyles (an Inspector of the Ministry), held an enquiry at the Town Hall to hear the case for and against the proposal. Mr. Hugh Gamon, barrister-at-law, of Liverpool, appeared for the applicant; the Town Council was represented by the Town Clerk (Mr. J. H. Dickson), and the Rural District Council by the Clerk (Mr. H. G. Williams). Mr. Ouseley Smith (Messrs. Potts, Martyn and Ouseley Smith), attended on behalf of residents of Upton.

Mr. Mottershead said it was his intention to use the grounds of Oakfield for a zoological gardens and aviary for foreign and English birds, and that it would be largely used for educational purposes. There would be a cafe for the convenience of visitors, but no form of attractions in the nature of "a fair." No large animals, such as lions, tigers or elephants, would be kept, and there would, it was argued, be no sort of disturbance, and nothing to interfere with the amenities of the parish.

After evidence for the applicant had been heard,

The Town Clerk said there could be no question at all that this property came within the purview of the Town Planning Order. This place, which was built as a residence, and always had been a residence, was to be suddenly turned into a zoological gardens, an aviary, and a cae. That must be a distinct development, and they could hardly have a stronger case for opposition. The property was to be turned into premises to be used for commercial purposes, and that being so, it was for the Town Planning Authority to decide in the first instance whether they would allow this to take place, and it was for the Ministry to decide whether that decision should be reversed. Upton always had been a residential

the public know what the scheme was. The Town Planning Committee turned it down before getting the full details and before hearing Mr. Mottershead. That was in great defiance to the circular received from the Ministry, and not a matter of common justice. The man had bought property for £3,500, and it was not common fairness to prevent his using it in the way he wished, without giving him the opportunity of stating his case. The opposition rested merely on the desire of keeping people from Upton. That was a perfectly impossible attitude this time of day with regard to a village in such close proximity to Chester. Chester was a city of which they were all proud, and they did all they could to invite people there, because it was good for trade. Yet, two miles out of Chester they did not want people. That was an attitude he would not call selfish so much as "old world" and in keeping with the old-world flavour of Upton.

Mr. Gamon and the Town Clerk thanked the Inspector.

The Inspector said he would visit Oakfield the next day, and any who cared to accompany him would be welcome.

Cheshire.
Observer.
Feb: 14/31.

4

'It was a long and anxious wait for the family'

George Mottershead drove home after shaking hands with the barrister and thanking his supporters. In a reflective mood he entered the kitchen to find his family waiting for news. He ran through the events of the day and a decision would not be reached for several weeks. The Inspector would visit the zoological gardens the next day.

Weary but resolved Mr Mott sat in the kitchen surrounded by his family. He began to talk to them about the final outcome of the court case. In his opinion the case for the opposition rested on objections to undesirable people who might come to Upton. It was not really about the keeping of animals and noises they might make. The villagers were concerned about the huge crowds, which would, they imagined, affect their lives as residents of the village.

But the district would grow in any case. Shops and houses would be built. It was all part of change and progress.

"The gardens will be managed on model lines," he mused. "I shall employ at least a dozen men to work on the grounds as gardeners and keepers. There will be no rowdiness of any kind. Do you think I would allow people to scamper about all over the place trampling down the beautiful flowers, shrubs and ornamental gardens?

"The aim will be to keep these gardens as tidy as any gentleman's residence in the country and the equal of any public park. I should be given credit for some common sense. The whole of the orchard adjoining the road will be preserved as a wild bird sanctuary."

Mr Mott rose from his chair, growing more animated every minute. June watched his every movement, in awe at her father's strength of conviction. She felt pride and love for him. She didn't understand the ramifications of the court proceedings but knew that what was happening was essential to the existence of the zoo, and vital to her father's vision.

"I have plans," he continued, "to cover some of these trees as an aviary in the future, when I have the funds to do so. Already the daffodils and narcissi are pushing through the earth. Do people really think that I would allow crowds of hooligans to trample everything into the ground? There will be proper supervision and a wise selection as to the class of visitors."

He warmed to his subject. "There is a huge misconception regarding the cafés. People think they will be like the roadside cafés. Nothing of the sort! We will provide teas and light refreshments for visitors. They will sit either inside the house or on the lawn. Teas will be served to tables and chairs will be provided so that the public can rest after wandering around the gardens."

And his anger rose as he imagined how things would be. "This house is beautiful. The stately rooms on the ground floor will be used for serving tea. The rooms are panelled - one in mahogany, another in American walnut and others in oak. It would be desecration to do any damage to these rooms."

Suddenly he looked weary.

"Time for bed now! Tomorrow I must be up and ready to show the Inspector the proof of what was said in court in support of our zoo."

The next day everyone tried to keep as busy as possible, and out of Mr Mott's way as he showed the Inspector around The Oakfield. He took great care to address the objections which had been raised at the hearing, and also took the opportunity to expand on the plans he had in mind to develop the property and the zoo.

So the fateful visit by the Inspector passed without event, much to everyone's relief, and it only took a day for all the family and helpers to be back into the solid routines of animal care and working in the gardens. It didn't take long for the inspection visit to fade into the background.

It had been a long and anxious wait for the family, but with spring came the good news they were waiting for. On March the thirteenth the Ministry of Health granted permission for the zoo to be opened subject to the conditions agreed upon with the City of Chester. Even then there was a lengthy delay before Chester City Council sent a copy of their conditions, meaning that the zoo could not open officially until June.

One of those conditions was that no advertisement or sign for the zoo could be placed on any lane or road in Cheshire. Only one sign could be erected, and that would be placed at the entrance to the zoo. Another condition was that if it closed for longer than six months, new planning permission for re-opening must be obtained.

It was very obvious that the Mottershead family and their zoo were not welcomed by the majority of the local public. The following week June was returning from the village shop when she heard laughter coming from behind a hedge. She turned quickly to see a group of children pointing at her and shouting rude remarks. A hail of small stones landed at her feet. She turned to run as one hit her in the back. Wiping the tears from her cheeks she vowed to keep the nasty incident to herself. She would tell no one.

The family were desperately poor and struggling to survive. One night June saw her mother bring down her jewellery box and the next day it was sold. Other household objects began to disappear, but feelings were kept hidden. Raising the cash was a means of survival and June knew not to ask for anything.

She spent her time skipping about between family members, watching her grandfather silently moving about in the gardens, feeding the goats and sitting watching the animals, following Mew around until she became a nuisance and finally returning to her mother's side to ask many questions.

This was a desperate time for the family. The zoo had been unable to open during the Easter and Whit holidays. Mr Mott was building pens and aviaries for the animals and birds, working desperately in the hope that they could open the gates in June. His lawyer advised a very quiet opening and no publicity during their first year.

Whipsnade Zoo had opened as an extension of London Zoo in May, both sides of the Houses of Parliament giving backing to the venture as London Zoo took advantage of a government scheme offering work at Whipsnade. It had extensive grounds, many animals and free publicity. Mr Mott was very envious.

The Mottershead family worked hard in readiness for an anticipated official opening. Her grandmother would take up her position at the newly built wooden pay box that was close to the Lodge, near to where a pond was to be constructed, so that visitors would be greeted by an enclosure containing water birds. June listened to the conversation over dinner, her father explaining that it must be dug by hand near to the entrance of the zoo in a small wild garden opposite the Lodge where June's grandparents lived.

"Can I help?" she interrupted.

"Of course, June, everyone must help," smiled her father as he leaned over and gave her a hug. "We will start tomorrow."

June awoke early but someone was already out in the gardens, where a spiral of smoke arose from the area where the pond would be. Clambering into her clothes and pulling on her old shoes she dashed out, but not before waking Mew and jumping down the stairs, landing with a thump in the passageway.

Her father's words rang through her ears: "Everyone must help", and finally she could join in, and show that she, too, could be really useful.

Running through the wet grass, she called out to her grandfather. He was building a bonfire, clearing the old garden ready for the pond to be dug. Together they chatted as he began to dig into the rich Cheshire soil, removing the thick grass sods, explaining all the time to June that beneath would be the hard red Cheshire clay. Already the little girl knew about the richness of the topsoil, fed by the leaf mould of countless autumns.

She popped all the worms and beetles; exposed by the digging, into a bucket, for later they would be fed to the lizards and other small creatures in the conservatory. Grandfather nodded with approval. He knew his little granddaughter well; she never missed an opportunity to provide food for the animals and she was fierce in her efforts to support the family's zoo.

June stepped gingerly onto the thick red soil and, to her great delight, her shoes oozed beneath the soft mud. But this time it wouldn't matter how muddy she became; she was helping. She plunged her hands into the red clay, noting with approval that the water was rising and turning everything into a glorious mud bath.

By the time the rest of the family arrived June was hardly recognisable. Even her hair and face were mud-splattered as she struggled to load the wheelbarrow with the slimy clay. Her father pushed the barrow up the wet planks and tipped the almost liquid earth out. A small hillock began to form and June was now standing below ground level.

With difficulty she pulled her shoes off, throwing them onto the bank, and felt the soft, thick mud ooze between her toes. As she pulled each foot out there was a wonderful slurping sound. Looking up, she stared into the somewhat disapproving face of her grandmother but she was now a worker like everyone else and basked in the silent approval of her family.

Eventually the pond was filled with muddy water on which could dabble and dive the beautiful Carolina and Mandarin ducks. A few days later some bossy Muscovy ducks were introduced.

Grandmother felt that it was her duty to look after the birds and a little ritual developed over the next few weeks. June sat by the pond and waited. Sure enough, out of the Lodge came grandmother, neatly buttoned into her coat. She wore her second best hat, carefully fitted on top of her tightly knotted white hair.

She carried stale bread for the ducks and, climbing to the top of the clay hillock, she threw it to the squabbling birds. June noted with approval that grandmother always made sure that the timid birds received their fair share.

Up until this point her grandmother had shown very little interest in the animals, concentrating on essential domestic duties instead but on this rare occasion she had taken responsibility for the pond.

One day, June sat watching her carry out the daily feeding of the birds. It was a warm morning after a night of rain that had soaked the ground. June watched idly as the dragonflies dipped over the water when suddenly she heard a strange noise, a slip-slopping sound. Looking up, she saw her grandmother slowly sliding down the mud, flat on her back and moving toward the pond in dignified but petrified slow motion.

June tried to call out in horror, but no sound came. Fascinated, she watched as grandmother was launched unceremoniously into the pond, vanishing beneath the red muddy water, leaving her second best hat floating on the surface.

Then she rose miraculously from the mire, her once white hair streaming down her back. But now it was stained red like the rest of her – even her cheeks were puce, as if she was blushing with great shame.

June turned and ran for grandfather and then on to the house. She did not return until she heard that granny was now safely seated by a roaring fire in the Lodge and quite safe. At last she ventured down to the duck pond to find grandad plodding about in the mud, retrieving a shapeless piece of sodden material – the hat.

June longed to be given a real job, one which she could do all on her own. She begged to be allowed to paint the bear pen black and the initial answer was a firm "No."

"Please, Mum," she begged. "I know I can do it; please, Mum."

Her mother left the kitchen, coming back with a sack. "Right, pull this on. I have cut a hole for your head and two for your arms. Here is a pot of black paint and a brush. Now get on with it and don't paint yourself whilst you are at it."

An exhausted but very happy little girl sat down for dinner that night, feeling part of the team despite being freckled with black spots on her face and hands. It was her zoo too and it was so important that she did her bit.

On June the tenth, 1931 Chester Zoo opened to the public.

The two girls dressed in their best clothes and watched for signs of activity at the pay box. They rose at dawn and walked round the grounds, feeling incredibly proud of their family's achievements.

They recalled the long, expensive legal battle which their father had won. They admired the café that their mother had created and walked about the mansion that had now been made into a home.

They wandered into the courtyard to look at the stables that now housed the animals. The Canadian black bears paced their new pen out in the courtyard, both glossy and happily now able to stand upright.

June ran quickly into the conservatory where the rustling sounds among the plants were evidence of fat toads and frogs. A little lizard ran across her shoe and into the fresh undergrowth. She joined Mew on the lawn where the peacocks displayed iridescent colours and pheasants roamed freely. The grass was short and springy and the paths well defined with not a single stray leaf.

For one brief moment June shut her eyes tightly, recalling that first night when the moon had lit up the solitary dog fox as he crossed in front of the huge red house. She turned and looked up at the windows and thorny columns of Pyracantha. Magic had happened here on The Oakfield estate.

So they waited, the entire family, for that wonderful moment when visitors would pour in, past the proud grandmother dressed in her finest black frock and bonnet, past the ornamental pond and along the pathways to the house and court yard.

31

No one came.

The Mottershead family had no words to exchange. Their disappointment and dismay were tangible. By midday only three or four people had passed through the pay box.

The pool which Granny fell into
(no. 26 on zoo map)

View of the Lodge at the main entrance to Chester Zoo

Granny at the pay box

5

'Animals must come first'

Mr Mott had connected a bell in the Lodge to a rope at the pay box and visitors were asked to pull the rope. This alerted grandmother who would rush out and take the money, a shilling for adults and sixpence for children. Over the next few weeks the bell rang very infrequently, much to the disappointment of the family. Life was rapidly turning into a financial nightmare for everyone involved.

During that long, difficult summer the family struggled on, ever determined to keep the zoo open at all costs. Grandfather grew vegetables and the autumn fruit provided food both for animals and family. And little June Mottershead finally had to face her first day at school. She was worried about this separation from the family, as she had never mixed with the local children.

Her mother had insisted on enrolling her in the Ursuline Convent in Chester. Despite tears and protests she endured her first day, resolute that she would hate school for it took her away from the zoo. Instinctively she knew that the family were in huge financial trouble and felt that she couldn't help them if she was locked away in a classroom.

But appearances must be kept up and the Mottershead family must appear to be solvent. June never talked about the zoo at school and there were so few visitors that she was relieved to find that none of her classmates knew about her unusual home. How could she explain the most amazing adventure of living in a zoo? She decided there and then that no one would believe her, so she took on two lives, the indifferent school routine and the thankful return every evening to the rich affirmation of her human and animal family.

Later that night she overheard her mother and father talking about the growing number of animals and the enormous cost of the zoo. Already money was being set aside from wages for unexpected bills whilst grandfather and grandmother existed on their ten shillings a week pension.

The family sat around the kitchen range where June's mother did the cooking for them each night. The conversation had been about the difficult financial situation, reminding June not to ask for the new fishing net she badly wanted, or the picture book of that mysterious Africa place – and definitely no new shoes. Besides, all the spare cash had been used to purchase her expensive school uniform.

As usual the conversation was interrupted time and time again by the different animals that wandered into the warm kitchen. An Amazonian parrot landed on the kitchen table only to be shooed away by June's mum. Wiping up parrot droppings from the floor was one thing, but it was quite another if and when they fouled the table. June looked around the warm kitchen with approval. It was rare to have all the family and live-in staff together at the same time as there was usually some sort of emergency whereupon one of them would have to rush out.

The growing number of new staff members who lived in at The Oakfield now occupied many of the spare bedrooms. The girls were housed in the nursery wing; the boys in the staff wing, and the parrots were placed between them!

Mew was eating her meal using only one hand, for cradled in her arms was a baby chimp, warmly cocooned in an old flannelette sheet. He was suffering from a cold, a problem that often afflicted the chimps, and Mew was determined that he would survive. Later she would carry him off to bed with her and wake in the night to feed him from a bottle.

June decided that it would be a wonderful idea if The Oakfield itself became the zoo as most of the animals seemed to be housed in its many rooms.

That night in the bedroom she shared with Mew she laid awake listening to the wheezing and small grunts from the baby chimp and to Mew's soft voice responding to him. She suddenly realised that her sister was using his language, replying in strange little guttural noises to his whimpering and sighing. It worked, for he fell asleep. How clever Mew was. Tomorrow June resolved to try out some monkey language. She would talk to the chimps when no one was about.

The following morning more chimps arrived from Liverpool. They had travelled on the shipping line owned by the Holt family and all of them were orphans. Gently they were lifted from their cages and placed in pens that had replaced the garages in the courtyard

Mew took charge, organising the fresh straw bedding, the food and a hand-knitted woollen blanket for each chimp. June did not realise at this stage that the mothers had been slaughtered in West Africa in order to acquire the baby chimps. Many of them were whimpering and one looked very sick, huddling in a corner and pressing itself against the wooden bench that was raised from the concrete floor.

"Mew, look at that one. Can I lift her out and look after her?"

Muriel had already spotted the sickly baby and nodded, as she was very busy housing the remainder of the animals. They hadn't been expected for at least another week and food had to be prepared immediately.

And so June and Mary met for the first time; the feeble little creature snuggled against the young girl's chest, responding to her heart beat as a human baby would. June saw immediately that the chimp was female; it was natural for her to identify the sex of the animals. Living in a zoo had taught her many things about the the natural world from an early age.

"I shall call her Mary," she announced proudly and immediately carried the fragile little creature to the warm kitchen. Here she found a cloth that she wound round Mary to make a nappy, and then she swaddled her quite tightly in soft warm flannelette.

Her mother watched approvingly.

"Now, June, feed her from this bottle, but only a little at a time. She is sick and her tummy is very small."

Lizzie bent down, listening carefully to the baby's breathing.

"Well, that's a relief. Her breathing is good at least. I do believe she is pining for her mother. Keep her close to you, June."

She smiled. June was glued to her little charge. There would be no separating them now. Unfortunately, within a few weeks Mary had caught a cold. As June had to go to school each day she was unable to do all the night duties required to keep the baby alive. Mew took over, waking in the night at all hours to give Mary little sips of warm milk and rubbing her chest with 'Vicks' to help her breathing.

The friendship between June and Mary grew as quickly as the chimp herself. She thrived on the motherly attention given by the little girl, often holding her hand and going for long walks around the zoo, looking in on the animals and chattering away. Sometimes she pulled June's hand to stop her when she wanted to look at something, at times she bounded ahead of the girl but always returned when called, flinging herself lovingly into welcoming human arms.

When June returned from school she changed quickly from her uniform, charged downstairs and straight to Mary's pen. Then off they would set together, either to play on the lawns in front of The Oakfield or to share apples from the orchard.

These were very happy times for June.

Mew mopped out the pens each day with disinfectant. Whilst they dried, the chimps came out to play, chattering in their own strange language. The zoo was closed every evening and during these times both girls would talk with the chimps, copying the basic sounds of their language and repeating the 'words'. It never seemed odd to talk in the animal language and this was many years before the scientific establishment woke up to its existence. Originally animals had been thought of as having no language and unable to use even basic tools.

Yet here at Chester Zoo in Upton two young girls made the discovery long before many others. No one ever heard them for they kept the chimp language quite secret. The sisters were shy with other people who would not understand but once the public was far away they entered quite freely into their animal communication.

When Mew scattered the fresh straw onto the pens each chimp reacted quite individually towards the new bedding. Some characters would throw their bedding into the air and mess up the entire pen; others would make a straw nest, curl up and snooze or clear the straw gently away until they reached the dry sawdust. Then with deft hands and fingers they would draw patterns in the dust and chatter to each other.

Mew made sure that each chimp had its own blanket. At night they would each have a cup of warm milk with a spoonful of malt and cod liver oil in it. She would say goodnight to them in their own language; they would answer back then sleep in their snug nests.

On a number of occasions a good friend of their father had advised Mew on medical advice for the chimps. Dr G. A Moulden was a council member who was devoted to the zoo. Nearly every weekend he visited The Oakfield with his pretty wife and three children, Gerald, Neville and Angela and it was then that he gave very knowledgeable advice on the rearing of the chimps. Of course there were no antibiotics to rely on for helping with the chimps' chest infections and Muriel was always relieved to see him if there was a problem. He became part of the growing support group concerned with the welfare of the animals and he and his family were welcomed into the Mottershead family. June loved to see him and his family at the zoo, enjoying his company for he was an extremely kind man who laughed often. He would remain an important participant in the zoo's progress and success for years.

Mary playing with June

June and Mary

Mary and Muriel

6

'Snap! Another lovely photo'

Shortly after, June's father decided to advertise for partners and on February the seventeenth 1932 a company was formed. Unfortunately this was under-funded from the start.

Mr Mott had heard from Dr English that the Shavington Zoo was closing down as it was losing money. The Mottershead family, hopeful of better times, were now able to sell the field that they owned there and offered to buy the stock.

The entire family were pleased to receive the animals, especially Babs the chimp who gave them a big hug and lots of kisses when she arrived at Upton. But Mr Mott had retrieved one new occupant from the Shavington Zoo, a very sad specimen indeed. He was Punch the polar bear, bought by the doctor from a circus, and he was in a shocking state. He was perhaps the dirtiest polar bear Mr Mott had ever seen. Despite the fact that Mr Mott's wife would now had to buy animal food from her housekeeping money, he could not bear to leave Punch to an uncertain fate and decided that the pathetic animal must come to Upton Zoo.

Mr Mott set about building temporary housing for the poor creature, until a pen could be built against the twelve-foot high kitchen garden wall. June helped her mother to carry the brass bedstead, which had been commandeered as reinforcement for the concrete.

He had convinced his family of Punch's future at Upton by describing the tiny bowl of water placed outside the old corrugated iron shed and within the cramped concrete enclosure where Punch was, at present, merely miserably existing.

When finally the dejected animal arrived, he looked more like a black bear. He gulped down his food then slumped on the ground, unresponsive to his surroundings. Punch remained indifferent to water. The icy seas of the Arctic were no longer a memory to him. They had been replaced by years of screaming circus spectators. Now he was simply a sideshow waiting to die.

Then one day the local hunt held its point-to-point race in Upton. They met outside the zoo's main gate and one horse fell at the first fence, breaking its neck. It was fresh meat and given to the zoo for food.

Piece by piece Mr Mott butchered it and stored it in a shed in the yard. He took a large chunk and presented it to Punch. The change in the polar bear was miraculous. He dived onto the fresh bloody meat and ripped it to bits. For several weeks he gorged on the horsemeat and, with a change in his diet, his memory seemed to return. He stamped and reared to his full height, acknowledging everyone around him. His health improved, if not his bathing standards and he grew powerful and strong.

Other amazing things were happening at the zoo. One weekend Mew called her father to the courtyard and June followed to see what was happening. Something very odd was taking place on the staircase, which went from the courtyard and up the tower, which was part of the entrance gate to the yard itself. June's first sighting of the strange animal was watching its head disappear back inside the window, as it could not possibly squeeze through it. The animal was far too large. It was, of course, Minnie the tapir. She was continually finding ways to leave her enclosure but on this occasion she had wandered into the courtyard. Climbing up the spiral staircase she reached the first window where she decided to make a quick exit. Now she was obviously seeking another route.

The full story was told shortly afterwards, recounted with laughter to the family over supper that night. Mew explained in detail the complicated rescue of Minnie. Mew had used another staircase on the other side of the arch, and then ran through a couple of rooms to the top of the spiral stairs. Minnie took up the entire space on the stairs! Mew spoke gently to her, as at her back end Mr Mott carefully lifted her back feet down one stair at a time until she was on ground level. Neither one could get past Minnie so it took at least two hours to bring her safely down. Life was never dull at the zoo!

Every day June arrived home to see changes – in people, animals and the routine running of the zoo. There was an air of optimism as more staff were employed, some of them locals but others who now lived in at The Oakfield.

Quickly she changed her uniform, dressing in her old comfortable clothes, and rushed off to find her big sister. Usually, by late afternoon Mew would be somewhere in the wilderness of plants, armed with a net and bottle, busy collecting insects and seeds for the birds. She carried a large paper bag into which she stowed all kinds of plants and June's immediate task was to help her by carrying and opening the bag as requested.

Mew would talk to her little sister but never about school, which was a relief to June. She hated it; from morning until the final bell she couldn't wait to leave. Too much was happening at The Oakfield and she was missing it.

Did June know that right at this very minute Miss Russell Allen was meeting with her father? She was helping with further finance and June knew that the Russell Allens, who lived at Davenham Hall, were vital to the survival of the zoo.

Her charming father was a clever businessman, whatever that meant. June wasn't really sure but she had heard the phrase often and it was connected with many visits away from the zoo, important visits which included her father dressing in smart new clothes and disappearing, sometimes for days at a time.

Back he would come with promises of new animals and offers of financial help. Only the day before he had talked over supper about the Holts, a wealthy Liverpool shipping family who were offering gifts of animals and birds from West Africa.

June only had a vague idea of such a place but during her dinner hour at the school she had investigated the whereabouts of Africa, discovering a picture book of wild animals, lions, elephants and monkeys. It was across the sea somewhere and that was enough information for the little girl. She pictured a Noah's Ark owned by the Holts sailing across the sea towards Chester. Maybe there would be lions too?

She shivered with excitement and anticipation. But, ever practical, Mew scolded her for dreaming.

"Come on, lazybones. Pick up the bag and let's get cracking. I want to feed the birds then check on the baby chimps. One of them has a cold and I might have to take him into the house overnight."

"Mew, can I play with the animals after closing time and will you play too?"

"You can play but I have too much work to do. Most of the smaller animals are wandering about now but remember, June, do not let the coati mundis out again. They cause such havoc if they are loose and they are very mischievous. We never know what they might get up to."

"Can I? Can I…?"

Mew anticipated June's wish. She knew her sister well.

"Go and find Minnie and have a ride on her. Soon you will be too heavy so make the best of it."

With that she strode towards the aviaries, June watching her stalk away on her long legs, her hair bouncing on her shoulders as she hurried off. June sighed. She knew her sister was beautiful. Ruefully she looked down at her old clothes then grinned when she stared at her shoes, remembering the muddy pond and her grandmother's drowned hat.

She set off through the orchard, reaching the lawn in front of the great red house. Not much had changed here. Yes, it was tidy but there were no curtains at the large windows. Animals came first. A peacock strode about on the stone steps, picking up crumbs from around the few wooden tables where her mother had served a few afternoon teas to the dwindling visitors. For business was still not good.

June went to the courtyard where Minnie the tapir lived, as solid as a pony but as bulky as a fully-grown pig. June nestled into her, stroking and scratching her head and neck. Minnie's bright little eyes stared in recognition and anticipation at the little girl. She nuzzled against June's frock.

"Yes, I know. Won't be a minute," and off June scampered, heading for the kitchen. She was soon back, taking a big bite from the apple, for she was hungry too.

Holding the apple flat on her hand she watched as the tapir's soft, pink mouth opened and Minnie's tongue licked at the fruit. Soon it was gone and then June gently slid her leg over Minnie's side until she was astride the warm creature. Putting her arms around Minnie's neck, she whispered, "Now take me for a little ride," and off they went towards grandfather's vegetables.

Grandad straightened painfully from his work on the lettuce bed.

"I see, come for a little treat have we?" and gently he fed the tapir with one of his vegetables. "Nearly too big for the horse, June," he called after her as they wandered off.

Their timing was perfect. As 'horse' and rider passed the steps, June's father and Geraldine Russell Allen were leaving the house. The lady laughed with delight at the little girl, begging for a photograph at the first opportunity.

"What a wonderful advertisement for the zoo!" she exclaimed.

Mr Mott already knew that his two lovely daughters would provide many photographs for the promotion of the zoo and noted that June needed new shoes. She looked like an urchin – a happy urchin but nevertheless poorly dressed. In the back of his mind he knew that the girls must appear on public occasions in smart clothes, to be used when photographs were taken with the animals. The public face of the zoo must be kept up at all costs but he said nothing of these thoughts to June as he saw Miss Russell Allen to her chauffeur-driven car.

As the car drove away, he turned to June, lifting her from the tapir's broad back.

She was held by his strong arms, her little hands around his neck. This was a rare moment for he was always so busy doing something somewhere.

"Dad," she whispered, "I love our zoo. We are doing well, aren't we? And dad, tell me about a land named Africa, which is a big zoo."

Together they sat on the bottom step of The Oakfield, her father describing some of the other lands where animals came from, drawing a geography lesson into the Cheshire earth to explain himself.

"But dad, who makes the money in those big zoos?"

"No, no, the animals run free, June. They live on the land, from the land. This is what I want here – animals that live as freely as we can manage to allow them to. Look at Punch, for instance."

"But I do, dad, I do."

"Well, what do you see?"

June thought hard, picturing Punch.

She hesitated. She didn't want to get it wrong. She wanted her father to feel proud of her.

"Well, he lies down a lot. He is very dirty and he won't go near his little pool that you made for him. I tell him every day but he won't take any notice of it apart from the drinking. Oh, and he won't talk to me!"

June's dad frowned.

"Animals don't talk to humans, June. That is not a good thing to encourage. They have their own lives." Then his voice softened as he realised that he had upset his little daughter. "But go on, June; you are doing well, carry on."

June thought very hard.

"Yes," she announced finally. "He is happier because he ate raw fresh horse meat. He loved it, dad. I lay by his pen and watched him rip it up."

"Correct, June, and did you notice anything about his teeth?"

"Yes. They were covered with blood but then he started to lick and clean himself and his teeth were shiny, just like me when I eat an apple. I think I understand, Dad. It was, it was . . ."

She searched for the word.

"Natural. It was natural for him, June. It has been a long time since Punch ripped up fresh meat. For a moment he forgot his circus days. He had his own kill, just like his parents and grandparents before him. They killed and ate on the great wilderness of ice, which we call the North Pole.

"It is so important, June, to try very hard to keep the animals as near to their natural life as possible. That is why our zoo always needs more money, so that we can build much larger enclosures and buy more land.

"Now run in and help your mother to prepare the supper. Tell her I won't be too long. I just need to check on some of the work being done on the new aviary."

Elizabeth Mottershead worked unceasingly in the kitchens, in the restaurant, with the young staff and across the grounds of the zoo. June often accompanied her as she checked on every animal before returning to cook the meal for family and staff.

Sometimes they reflected on Shavington, her mother smiling and waving her hand towards the ever-expanding grounds and gardens.

"Yes, June, it is a struggle. Sometimes things are so hard. We are building our zoo because we work together. You are a good girl and..." She paused as June looked up questioningly. "What is it you want, June?"

She knew her daughter well.

"Mum, it's my shoes. They're worn out. I only have my school ones that are any good. Can I wear them after school instead of saving them?"

June blushed with shame. She had made a secret vow not to ask for anything.

"Well, as a matter of fact your dad and I had a little talk last night. We will be going into Chester one evening after school finishes for smart clothes and shoes for both of you. Of course your sister is grown up now and can choose her own clothes but I will help you."

June was astonished. This had never happened before; most of her clothes were hand made. Her expensive convent school uniform had been made to last but when she had rushed through the gardens she had accidentally ripped it.

"Why?" was the only word she could manage.

"Well, your Dad thinks you are both looking a bit shabby. Your smart clothes will be used for special times when we have visitors, and in particular for photos. We don't want the world to think we are poor, do we?"

June skipped ahead happily. The thought of new clothes bought from a proper shop was too exciting for words. She didn't care why they were to be bought and, anyway, it made her feel a very vital part of the public face of the zoo. She would be important! The following week, dressed in a new cardigan, pretty cotton frock and wearing those longed-for new shoes, she posed with Mary for photographs in front of The Oakfield.

This was followed by a picture taken with a very large macaw, which leaned his big face against June's forehead; they were old friends and he was happy to pose. June arranged her hands to be neatly clasping each other and, on instruction from her father, she turned sidewards. Her short dark hair had been brushed and her untidy fringe clipped to one side.

The result was a whimsical photograph of a very pretty little girl and a large tropical bird ... ideal for promotional purposes!

She followed her father to the bear pit where she stretched out an arm high above the Malayan bear, calling him to her. As she had fed him from a baby he obliged, looking up expectantly and waiting for the titbit that would be dropped. Snap! Another lovely photo! There would come a cold wintery day when the snow piled so high inside the pit that he simply walked up the ramped snow and out into the relative freedom of the garden.

These promotional sessions would continue over the years, but June would not be so approving of the posing as time went on. Neither would her sister. However, these were early days and they didn't question the reasons behind many things. The most important fact was to make a successful zoo, the finest in the world, and survive as a family.

June was beginning to feel very conscious of her unusual family home, keeping very quiet at the convent. She never volunteered to talk to the class, chose her few friends with care and very rarely brought a girlfriend to play at the zoo.

One day, though, she did bring a friend home to play. All day they fed Minnie the Tapir, playing with her on the lawn. June's friend was persuaded to take rides on Minnie but she slipped off several times, not really liking the experience. She was lighter than June who was now too heavy for Minnie. But the friend was not used to the strange animal and demanded to be lifted from the warm, comfortable back.

June realised that the entire zoo must seem quite different to her friend. She saw that the little girl was scared of the animals, a feeling she could hardly comprehend. They could share the laughter but not June's own feelings towards her extended 'family'.

On a visit to her friend's house she hurried into the garden to look for a zoo but found only neat lawn and beds of roses. Everyone laughed when she asked where her friend's animals were.

This was a turning point in June's life for she had never considered her family as being different in any way from other people. She was shy so didn't talk about her animal friends but she was quickly becoming aware that the Mottersheads were unique, and not just in Upton or even as far as Chester. The world of animals was coming to them from every exotic environment. No wonder her father strode about looking serious at times. No wonder her mother worked from dawn until dusk and her sister fell exhausted into bed each night.

But June had no one to confide in. She did not trust humans as much as animals.

One early autumn evening the zoo closed and became their home once again. All visitors had left. June climbed down from the wooden apple crate where she had stood in order to reach the counter. It was placed just inside the main door of The Oakfield, where her mother had set it up – a counter that held snacks of liquorice, boiled sweets, biscuits and chocolate. June was expected to sell these to the small number of visitors, for business had been very poor during the summer. There never seemed to be sufficient money yet more and more animals kept arriving, animals that had been bought as pets and had outgrown their welcome.

June was hungry but knew that she could not eat the food. Every penny earned was needed and anyway, it would be supper at 6pm. She must wait.

She wandered out towards the large pen that housed Punch, the polar bear. She knew that she must never enter his home for although he lay about, rolling over from time to time like a giant dirty teddy bear, he could be very fierce. She remembered the horsemeat and how he had torn into it.

Lying down on the concrete, she stared into Punch's eyes. He loped across the pen towards the little girl, slumping against the side of the enclosure. She spoke softly to him.

"Hello, Punch. Today I am going to tell you a little story about the North Pole. I know where it is. Are you listening, Punch?"

Staring into his unfathomable blue-black eyes, two bright little pebbles set into such a magnificent head, she kept total eye contact for the entire talk. She felt he understood every word. He didn't have to talk.

"I am sorry, Punch. Sorry you are dirty and you need a bigger home and a big pool with an iceberg floating in it .... because that is what they are called, those big lumps of ice in your land. You were born there, you know... on the ice. Your mother hunted for seals and fed you out there."

She frowned, deciding not to tell him any more about what might have happened to his mother. She could hear his strong breathing as he studied her intently. A fly landed on his rubbery nose but he ignored it.

"It isn't easy for me either, Punch. I don't like school, you see. I shouldn't actually be there. I am in a pen in that classroom and I hate it. No one ever listens to what I want to do. I have to go there every school day."

Her voice rose, as she grew angry. Punch never flinched, hanging onto every word. "And I am hungry. Like you I have to wait for someone to feed me."

Once again she decided diplomatically not to mention the word 'mother'.

"Now I am going to tell you a secret. One day you will have a new pen. There will be more water in it and maybe you will wash and become snowy white like the picture in my new book that I had for Christmas. Tomorrow I shall bring it here and show you a photo of how you could look if you wanted to."

The pebble eyes never flinched. Intent on June's voice the enormous shaggy creature was totally still and silent.

"I am sad for you, Punch. I am sorry. You should be in that place called the North Pole. You shouldn't be here at all, or in a circus."

She lowered her voice; glancing round to make sure no one was listening.

She leant forward, feeling his warm animal breath on her face. She had never been so close to him before but he was a good listener and he cared, she knew he cared.

"I don't like to see you in a pen."

There, she had said it even though she felt very guilty indeed. Only she and her friend Punch would ever know.

"See you tomorrow, Punch," and she ran off quickly into The Oakfield wondering why she felt so shaky inside.

'Animals are much nicer than human beings', she thought defiantly.

Punch the polar bear arrived from Shavington Zoo when it closed

June had grown too big to ride on Minnie the tapir
so her friend sat on her

June with Rob Rob the red and blue macaw

7

'What's an orphanage?'

1933 brought more unwelcome reminders of the on-going struggle for survival. Mr Mott endeavoured to keep everyone's spirits up by reminding them of the growing success of and support for the zoo. They must be patient and everyone must work hard.

After supper one night he announced the imminent arrival of another helper, a boy from the Frodsham orphanage. He would sleep in the room over the kitchen with two other boys who helped in the grounds.

A boy from an orphanage! June roused herself, turning from the warmth of the stove where she had been dozing. She nudged Mew.

"What's an orphanage?"

"Where children go if they cannot be looked after at home or if they have no parents," whispered her sister, who was now listening anxiously. She was thinking of her mother and yet another mouth to feed.

"He will be fine. There is a lot to be done. The people at the orphanage say he is keen on gardening and a willing worker, and grandad needs more help."

June was thinking about the animals. Many of them were orphans, so what would be the difference? She liked the sound of this new arrival.

"How old is he, Dad?" she enquired.

"Just a few years older than you. He's just finished school so he's happy to move out of the orphanage and join us. What do you think?"

No answer was necessary, as there was a comfortable silence around the table.

"Good. His name is Charlie and he will be dropped off here on Monday. He will have plenty of opportunity to learn about gardening from grandad. You know I am of the opinion that anybody can do anything if given the opportunity."

'Yes', thought Mew, 'and particularly if they're given no choice.' She was brooding over the fact that her mother was the immediate and essential carer of the welfare of all the animals in the zoo.

That night June fell asleep to dream of orphans, a new brother and, curiously, an aquarium where she could gracefully swim with the myriad rainbow of fish.

Within a few days Charlie arrived from the orphanage with his few belongings, to be greeted by the other girls and boys already working at the zoo. In the kitchen, Charlie sat wide-eyed in amazement at the variety of animals that wandered through the rooms looking for anything edible in the warmth of the house.

"Well, Mrs Mottershead, this is a right place. It belongs to everyone and no one. I'll fit in here, no doubt about it!"

And he certainly did, although that first night was a very strange experience for him, sharing the room above the kitchen with the two other boys; he lay awake for a long time listening to the sounds of animal calls, inside and outside the great mansion.

"Parrots in the bedroom next door," he muttered but the boys were asleep. Already old hands at the zoo, nothing surprised them or kept them awake. Charlie was so cold that he had gone to bed with two hot water bottles, a jumper and long socks. Little did he know that he was sleeping in the warmest bedroom in the house!

"Well," he said quietly to himself, "never thought about big posh houses being so cold. Not so grand after all," but he smiled contentedly as he fell asleep with a full stomach and a happy heart. No longer institutionalised, he would be a free and working man next morning.

He was certainly that. Woken by the boys at 6.00 a.m., he was given the job of helping Grandad to double-dig the kitchen garden. Then it was sweeping paths, burning rubbish and getting to know this old man who resembled Father Christmas. grandad was an expert and willing to train the young man. They were still hard at it when June raced back from school. She had missed him the night before and was curious to meet the 'new' brother.

The two young people stared at each other, and then Charlie beamed.

"Never had a sister," he explained by way of an introduction.

"Well, you have now. Come with me and I will show you around if grandad will let you go."

Her grandfather smiled. It was good to see June with someone nearer her age. Sometimes he thought she was too much on her own. Off the two strolled, disappearing in the direction of the courtyard. Some time later Charlie had been shown most of the zoo, accompanied by an unusually talkative June. A life-long friendship had begun. Such was the charming allure of the Mottershead family and their zoo world within a garden.

Shortly after Charlie's arrival a new animal arrived, donated by the Duke of Westminster, a capybara from Brazil.

"What is it, Dad?" June was immediately curious.

"It is the largest rodent in the world, looks like a giant guinea pig but with longer legs and lives on the same kind of food, so it should be easy and cheap to feed."

He chuckled to himself.

"The Duke bought him as an exotic pet but never knew that he could swim. Put him out on an island in the river Dee. Of course, being aquatic, he just swam across. The Duke's staff would round it up, return it and the animal would just swim back.

"So now we have the capybara and the Duke's friends can come here to visit it. All good news for the zoo! 1933 has been a promising year for us and we are gaining support and more animals everyday."

For months the Mottershead family worked around the clock, hoping to turn around the finances, trying desperately to realise Mr. Mott's vision of the zoo. No one had a single day off work as they all struggled to exist. Animals, the gardens and family all had to be kept but with what? The Chester Zoological Society, the name under which Mr Mottershead had established their business, was failing. As hard as the immediate family, relations on both sides of the family and unpaid helpers tried, very few visitors arrived, unlike the bills, which regularly served to remind June's mother and father that the zoo might never succeed.

Finally the Chester Zoological Society Ltd went into voluntary liquidation. The family knew that if the zoo closed it would be lost forever. At just six years of age, June did not understand the full implications of the bailiffs finally paying a visit to The Oakfield but was aware of the anxiety in both her parents.

It happened one weekend when she helped her mother in the kitchen where scones and tea were prepared. She sensed the tension as her mother finally carried out the tray to the morning room. It was here that her mother convinced the two dark suited visitors that her husband would return shortly from his business trip, and would pay the money owing. June's father had spent weeks trying to raise five hundred pounds in cash leaving £5,150, which remained outstanding on mortgages together with a series of debentures.

Miraculously, Mr Mott arrived with the money and the bailiffs left. Only then did June's mother reveal her despair, sinking into a chair by the empty afternoon tea tray. Once again the zoo had been saved, yet the Chester Zoological Society Ltd still wanted closure. The loans needed to be paid back as the financial future for the business did not look at all promising.

Mr Mott knew that money could be made quickly by betraying his dream and allowing the zoological gardens to become a place where 'lower' forms of entertainment for people could bring in much needed funds. But he did not want this for he believed fervently in the dignity and relative freedom of the captured animals. He was a man well before his time and his vision drove him to seek an answer through further investment. He wanted a non-profit organization, which would run the zoo as a society and for this he would need financial support, which he hoped would come from his supporters and friends who also believed in his dream. 1934 would be a very important year for the zoo.

The famous Belle Vue Zoo at Manchester was a prospering business, which was now very popular. The firm that ran it had a dirt track motorcycle circuit, an international circus every Christmas and a huge firework display in November. It also had a fairground and a zoo where most of the animals were behind bars. It was a financial success and the public flocked there.

During his business meetings, Mr Mott and the director of the zoological part of Belle Vue became firm friends. Mr Illes was a glamorous handsome man with a charming manner. Dark haired and with a lovely smile, he was in June's eyes the perfect gentleman. Inspired by her father's vision he began to visit the little zoo. She saw him many times, walking about the gardens with her father, both of them engrossed in conversation. He was very sincere and polite to all the family and staff, wanting only the best for them.

On several occasions June visited the famous zoo of the North of England with her father. An outing to Belle Vue was always a treat for the family who travelled by car and were treated extremely well by Mr Illes, who was now a firm friend of the family.

The two men would walk ahead round the zoo, deep in discussion of future plans, whilst June trailed behind looking at the many animals which were not at Chester. She stared inside the cages, inspecting everything, delighted to see the hippos and giraffes housed in a large high roofed building with stalls for the different animals. The hippos had a pool, which they wallowed in and all of them were kept indoors. Finally she reached the elephants, the first time she had seen such strange animals as they plodded about. Laughing with delight she stared at their leathery bodies and huge flapping ears. How she would love to see elephants at home in her zoo! The deer and antelopes had outdoor runs, which were very well kept. It was obvious that much money had been spent for the enterprise was a considerable one.

Mr Illes kindly gave the family tickets for the firework display, delighting everyone, for the circus and family outings were the highlights of the year for the struggling Mottershead family. June and her father went on their own on two occasions. Mr Illes took them to the Palm Restaurant inside Belle Vue Zoo where they were served by waiters in formal wear. June was quite overwhelmed, feeling like a very posh lady as she sat at the table, her napkin placed neatly on her knee and offered the menu to make her choice of meal.

As she ate, she stared around her at the luxurious fittings, noting her father and his friend talking earnestly together as always, and she felt reassured about the future of her zoo.

Mr Illes became the first financial backer of Upton Zoo, and along with Miss Russell Allan he initially saved it from closure. They were an inspiration to Mr Mott who began writing to industrialists, wealthy local people who were intrigued by the venture and visitors who had shown a sincere interest in the zoo, asking them if they would lend money to support a non-profit making society. All future profits would be ploughed back into the business until it became fully self-supporting.

Initially there was little interest shown, but Mr Mott already had the financial backing from two acquaintances sympathetic to his endeavours and was encouraged to go ahead. So he set up the North of England Zoological Society, which was registered as a non-profit sharing company, to be operated as an educational and charitable institution as from the ninth of May 1934. The Society took over the running of the zoo on June the thirteenth 1934, when members were invited to pay one guinea a year, giving them free admission to Upton Zoo; the first meeting of the Society being held that same day.

However, the debts mounted and for years it was an uphill struggle for this new venture, but slowly interest did grow, for Mr Mott's dream had begun to spread. Wealthy people appreciated the enormous struggle and effort made by the family and wanted to help. Once they had met Mr Mott they were caught up in his vision, recognising his tenacity and determination to succeed through his powerful work ethic and the backing of his family. They recognised that this was a 'first' in zoo history and wanted to be a part of it.

At that first meeting, in June 1934, June's father was appointed Director/ Secretary and paid a salary of £3 a week. His wife was made catering manageress and paid a salary of £1 a week. Mew was made assistant curator with a salary of ten shillings a week and the entire family received free lodgings and their food. June's grandparents had the Lodge as their home, and her grandfather looked after all the gardens with no pay.

When the society took over there was only £13 in the bank and the family remained poor for years. But the zoo was saved and the dream could be realised without the terrible worry of closure.

Mr Mott took out a second mortgage and bought two narrow strips of land, one of which was in a field adjacent to the main house and courtyard. Fortunately for the zoo, this field was developed into a riding school and would play an important part in future plans for the expansion of the zoo. The other piece of land, a small square between the Lodge and the road, was purchased for a car park.

Mr Mottershead with the capybara given to the zoo
by the Duke of Westminster

8

'A ghostly tale'

Within days a new bird collection arrived for the zoo, donated by Miss Esther Holt, a member of the shipping line family from Liverpool. It was a very personal gift as the collection had belonged to her. The zoo was given a boost in confidence as the birds, including some very rare and beautiful finches, were rehoused in their new aviary. The lengthened flight cage had been thoughtfully positioned in the part of the conservatory that housed the vinery, but plans had already been made for a walk- through aviary to be built the following year.

Miss Holt also kindly provided a weekly amount of money with which to buy the very expensive seeds and fruit that constituted the birds' required diet.

Muriel prepared the tropical fruit for the birds, slicing it before placing it in the aviary. June longed for a taste. Her mouth watered as her sister prepared it.

"Please, Mew, can I have some?"

"You are a pest, June. You know that Miss Holt pays for it for her birds. They won't be sitting down to supper. Don't be greedy."

"I am not greedy but I really would like some banana and a taste of that orange you are peeling. Please, Mew. One little bit won't matter."

Mew handed her two small pieces of fruit and June ran off quickly. Not looking where she was going, she bumped into a man as she turned the corner towards the house.

"Oh, I'm so sorry," she gasped in mid-flight, rushing off to see Punch.

Later she saw him again, talking to her mother. Both were smiling so it couldn't be too concerning. June remembered the visit from the bailiffs even though that had been months ago. The family were very wary of officials but always polite.

Over dinner that night she heard her mother explaining just who the stranger was.

"Believe me George it came as a bit of a shock," she explained to her husband. "He'd been around for most of the day. I remember because I served him a salmon salad out on the lawn around midday. He was asking me lots of questions then."

"Didn't you even suspect who it might be?" questioned Mr Mott.

"No, why would I? He laughed when I told him how the parrots lived inside on the cooler nights and always during the winter. He seemed to think it was a good idea. Then I was discussing the new arrivals and that is when a certain little girl almost knocked him over!"

She smiled at June.

"He knew who you were, June," she said as June lowered her eyes, "because later on he saw us together."

"But Mum, who was he?" Muriel was growing impatient with the mystery.

"Only the Marquis of Tavistock! He wanted to find out for himself how the birds were kept."

The room was silent. They all knew that at this delicate point of survival the zoo was ill prepared to take on board too much criticism.

Lizzie laughed.

"Stop worrying! He was very pleased indeed! He was so pleased in fact that he has given us a pair of Western black cockatoos from his collection. Not only that, but he actually defended our zoo to a visitor who was complaining that the new finches had too much room. Surely, she said, it would be bad for them to have so much flight when they were more secure in small cages. Well, the Marquis explained all about the zoo, how it was trying to be as close to the wild as it could be, and that was why the animals and birds are so happy.

"The visitor didn't stay long after that. Some people have no idea; they think animals must be tightly confined."

Everyone laughed. They needed good news.

But June knew here was an opportunity to speak up.

"Well then, what about Punch? He is squashed into that little pen. When can he have more room and water that he can swim in?"

"Oh, oh, so our little girl is fighting for the animals." Her father ruffled June's hair. "As soon as we can manage it he will be rehoused. Now, talking of birds, whereabouts is Pelly?"

The family all smiled. They knew Pelly the pelican very well indeed. Although the bird's wings were clipped every twelve months, Mr Mott had forgotten to do so this particular year and Pelly had taken to the air, rising high above the zoo. They had watched in growing consternation and Mr Mott had cursed his forgetfulness. Higher and higher flew the huge bird until he was a mere speck over the Cheshire countryside.

'Goodbye Pelly!' they all thought, until the telephone calls started to come in. He had been sighted over the river Dee, then over the cathedral and finally he had been spotted on the Dee at Eaton Hall, the home of the Duke of Westminster. Would Mr Mottershead please collect him?

Mr Mott and Mew drove beyond Chester but by the time they reached the place where Pelly had been sighted, the bird had taken off, heading for his home at The Oakfield. His instinctual memory served him well. He landed gracefully by the door of the back kitchen then waddled inside, calling very loudly and demanding to be fed! He would not stop squawking until his bucket of fish was produced.

Over two hours later a tired and rather cross Mr Mott drove up. It was a story told many times amidst much laughter. After all, they teased their father; didn't he want a zoo without bars? Obviously Pelly must have overheard him.

Unfortunately, the Mottersheads were reminded that not all animals that roamed beyond the sanctuary of the zoo were as fortunate as Pelly had been.

Another member of the zoo used to fly freely across the village of Upton, searching for seeds in the nearby fields. Locals used to spot Honky the crowned crane. He became quite a local but he always returned to the zoo after lunch. The family grew to expect his return as down he came, habitually landing on The Oakfield lawn, hungry and ready to be fed his corn.

One day he did not return. Mew was out scanning the sky when June returned from school. Their mother joined them but no big bird appeared.

The following day he was still absent resulting in a search party who set out from the zoo to look for him. Sadly, they spotted Honky floating in a nearby pond, killed by shotgun pellets. He was brought home and given a burial in silence and sadness.

It was an ugly reminder that potential hostility and even cruelty lay in wait for their animals beyond the sanctuary of the zoo grounds.

The very next day Mew discovered a group of boys teasing the chimps by running up and down outside their enclosure, imitating their walking and language. The chimps were highly agitated but not as much as the boys were when Mew collared them. They were shown out of the zoo immediately after Mew had taken their details and the name of their school.

She was a formidable ally of all the animals but in particular of the chimps, most of which she had lovingly hand reared from babies.
June knew how determined her sister could be when it came to defending the animals. Only a few days before she had witnessed a discussion between her father and Mew.

She was wandering in the chimp house when she heard them, Mew pleading with her father. No one noticed June as she watched and listened.

"Please, Dad, we will lose two of the baby chimps if you insist on the heating being turned down. The nights are too cold and they have bad chests."

59

Her father sighed. "We cannot afford to keep turning the heaters up every time an animal gets sick. We haven't sufficient funds to do it. Give them an extra blanket."

"But the chimps will suffer, Dad. I won't let them. If necessary I will bring them all into The Oakfield with me. They can all sleep in my bedroom. Yes, that's the answer."

"Don't be ridiculous Mew. We can only do our best," retorted her father but Mew wasn't satisfied until money was found for more heating. She took her position as animal keeper very seriously indeed and felt fiercely responsible for their welfare.

Later that evening she walked around the grounds with her mother who always checked the animals before supper. Lizzie broached the subject of the heating. "Don't argue, Mew. It will only make matters worse. Money's tight and it's a struggle to keep the zoo going. Your father is very worried. Now, you and I have saved some money in case there isn't enough cash to pay the staff, haven't we?"

"Yes, Mum," Mew agreed, already trusting her mother to do the right thing.

"Right!"

Lizzie was resolute. The animals had been given to the zoo, placed in their care, and none of them would suffer if she could help it.

Mew smiled, the smile of a maturing young woman now, a paid member of staff who had an opinion that was worth listening to. She knew just what her mother was hinting at.

"Thanks Mum!"

"Come on; let's find that sister of yours. I know where she will be – lost in the orchard no doubt! Now, no further mention of this! We will do what we feel is best. Haven't we always done?"

Mew looked at her mother, a strong determined woman, and she marvelled at her compassion, love and strength. She hoped she would grow to be like her. No other mother would struggle and work harder than she did, so often on her own as her husband was always so busy elsewhere and involved with business deals and strangers. Where did her mother get her strength?

The zoo was growing every day but many strange little incidents were occurring! One Saturday night a monitor lizard disappeared from the reptile house. The keeper discovered that the creature was missing when he was making his evening walks. How could such a considerable creature, measuring some twenty-four inches from his nose to his tail, simply disappear?

Everyone searched with no success. Even the water pool was drained but no lizard could be found.

Finally attention focused on the Indian python, which was the largest of the snakes apart from the anaconda. Had he eaten the lizard? The keeper had the unpleasant task of cornering the enormous snake. Feeling purposely along its body he soon could trace the bony limbs of the lizard inside it!

The monitor had recently been described in the local press as an 'old world' reptile with powerful-clawed limbs. There must have been a fierce battle to the death between the two creatures.

Shortly after this bizarre incident a seven-foot snake narrowly escaped death as a result of over eating. The keeper noticed that it was missing but in the corner of the cage was a small rat hole. Several days later a gardener spotted the head of a snake sticking out of a rat hole near to the path. Part of the path was removed revealing the enormously bloated snake. He had eaten so many rats that he was unable to return down the hole by which he had entered!

Shortly after these incidents, a ghostly tale began to circulate amongst the villagers of Upton. A young couple were standing by a gate in a lane near to the village when they were startled by a noise that resembled the rattling of chains! Suddenly something strange scuttled across the path in front of them.

Unnerved by the noise and the sudden appearance and disappearance of something they couldn't identify in the dusk, they moved on quickly. Then they heard approaching excited talking and a raised voice.

"I tell you, you've had more than is good for you."

A man's voice replied. " …. And I tell you I distinctly heard something like chains dragging along the ground." It was another couple, evidently just as startled and mystified.

The two couples met up and discussed the weird incident but had no answers. As they were talking together, they were startled as a mystery creature ran across the gloomy path and disappeared into the undergrowth. Shortly after this another walker appeared. He had also seen the creature, suggesting that it might be an animal which had escaped from the zoo.

Not convinced, they quickly returned down the path and were soon in the village pub telling their 'ghost' story.

The strange spooky animal turned out to be Penelope the porcupine, the wife of Paul porcupine. They were old residents of the zoo. Mew had helped to rear Penelope and June had often seen the prickly creature nestled on her sister's knee.

Recently though, Penelope had developed a wanderlust, tunnelling successfully out of her enclosure. This first attempt resulted in the complete collapse of her home but undeterred she continued her tunnelling a few weeks later, working her way out of a new enclosure.

This time the escape was successful but keepers discovered that she returned to the zoo each night to visit Paul her mate. The search was called off and two keepers waited for her nightly return journey, finally capturing her.

The noise resembling clanking chains was caused by the porcupine's tail as she scampered about, it was no wonder people thought she was a ghost!

June with Pelly the pelican

The 'ghost' of Chester Zoo, Penelope the porcupine

9

'Parrots in the bedroom'

For three years the zoo struggled to stay open, yet the number of animals grew. Support came from many sources. As well as ordinary individuals who loved animals, wealthy Cheshire people also took an interest in the continued struggle of the Mottershead family to keep their noble concientious dream of a zoo alive. Although members of the Mottershead family still referred to 'Upton Zoo' it was now generally known to the public as Chester Zoo. Its original name slipped away over the next few years as it became steadily associated with the City of Chester.

On the 3rd September 1934 June was given the task of presenting Lady Daresbury with a basket of flowers. The official occasion marked the opening of the first cold water aquarium at Chester Zoo. Installed beneath The Oakfield were six cold-water tanks, placed in the wine cellar. The aquarium had been paid for by Miss Russell Allan. June had watched the fitting out of the tanks, enjoying going down into the cellars that were dark and spacious. So it was with enthusiasm that she made the presentation.

Feeling extremely important she stepped forward to make her short speech. She wore her 'photograph' clothes and new shoes. Hidden inside the flowers that she carried was a can holding tropical fish, bought especially for Lady Daresbury. The fish tin was wrapped in newspapers and a warm cloth to preserve the temperature of the water. There were of course no tropical fish at the zoo and the gift was rather special.

Once the ceremonial welcome was over she quickly changed her clothes and rushed off to tell Punch all about the important events. He listened, staring steadfastly into the little girl's eyes as she described her part in the important occasion.

Then she made her way to the wire cage that housed the two bears from Matlock. Eve was sleeping but Adam came over to the little girl. At full height he was huge. June climbed up onto the safety barrier and leaned over to tell him about the day's events.

Her knowledge of far away countries was expanding. She felt confident to talk to Adam about North America, his homeland where he had roamed as a cub, never far from his mother. In her newly acquired illustrated atlas June had seen black and white photographs of the forests and rushing streams of this country. She imagined Adam sniffing the icy water and plunging in to catch fish. All these facts she reiterated again and again but did not remind him of the cave at Matlock, his torture chamber which he had shared with Eve.

And, as with Punch, she did not mention his mother or what might have happened to her.

The meal that September evening was full of family chatter about the day's successful events, despite the quickly depleting funds. The zoo was losing money and there were mouths to feed, human and animal, hundreds of them now if all the birds were counted.

June and her sister moved closer to the stove. The Oakfield was growing colder as winter approached. Some animals must once again come inside the house during the frosty nights.

During the weeks that followed there were exciting developments at the zoo. Miss Geraldine Russell Allen came to see the development of the aquarium and following her visit she contacted George Mottershead yet again as she was an enthusiastic member of the council, supporting all the new changes which were taking place.She always attended the council meetings in the evenings, arriving in her chauffeur driven car. She would ask her chauffeur Sam to take the car with some of the staff and drive into Chester to the cinema. She paid for everyone and Sam would return them to the zoo, pick Miss Russell Allen up at the end of the meeting and take her home. She was much loved by everyone at The Oakfield.

Her friend Mr Grousell, a quiet and unassuming man, visited every Sunday morning from his home in Heswall and he and Mr Mott would tour every part of the zoo, discussing what further developments were affordable. They would walk slowly all around the zoo, discussing its problems, deciding what needed to be done and what to bring up at the monthly council meetings.

The subject of available money for buying land, building and purchasing animals was raised during these walks. He was a distinguished looking man, rather tall, and quietly spoken. He never pushed himself forward yet he was greatly liked and respected as he walked about the grounds speaking to the staff. He was easily recognised, invariably wearing a grey suit and tie. June loved to talk to him as his extremely polite manners fascinated her. He had no children and was obviously not used to them, but his enthusiasm for the zoo was very apparent.

Her parents spoke very highly of him as his sincerity and belief in their plans was consistent. Mr Mott appreciated his sound advice and friendship. He was quick to point out any fancy idea, which was not practical and would not work, quietly pointing out its drawbacks. Mr Grousell never seemed to stay for lunch unlike many of Mr Mott's friends. June often watched him head for the car park, feeling sure that he was returning home to Mrs Grousell as her mother had told her that they had no children of their own. He often spoke lovingly about the animals for they were his chief concern over the many years he worked towards the success of the zoo.

It seemed as if support from one wealthy family was quickly followed by donations from another source. June knew her father was right. Appearances had to be kept up in order for the outside world to believe in their dream.

There was another Charlie at the zoo; a penguin, which had lost his mate but it was too expensive to buy another one. Miss Russell Allen had presented the zoo with two penguins but unfortunately the female had died within two weeks of arrival leaving Charlie a widower.

Grandad was the first to notice that Charlie had begun to pine and the Mottersheads anticipated the penguin's death. Fortunately a visitor noticed Charlie's solitude and approached one of the keepers with an offer to hand over her pet penguin, which could be collected from her home on the other side of Preston. It was a female, but when the penguin arrived at Charlie's enclosure she was reluctant to enter the water.

Mr Mott explained to June that it was probably because several ducks were using the same pool. The penguin was named Sadie and she joined Charlie in his pen where he totally ignored her, probably because she was very muddy. June laughed, thinking of Punch. Now they had two animals that refused to bathe.

Maybe realising that she was not at her best, Sadie at last took to the water and refused to come out unless fish arrived. Nevertheless, the two penguins practically ignored each other and never fed together.

Early in 1935 Charlie began to build a nest of stones as penguins do in the wild. He proceeded to sit on it for days and hoped to encourage Sadie. When she did not respond he drove her into the hole and guarded the entrance. She sat there for several days until she laid two eggs. From that moment Charlie fussed over her, considering her to be his true mate. The eggs hatched and they had two thriving chicks.

They fed the babies beak to beak for ten months, regurgitating the whole herrings which had been given to them by hand at feeding time. Whilst the babies were still dependent on the parents they produced two more eggs but Sadie could not manage to sit on them and feed the chicks. Shortly afterwards June spotted her in the pen, floating dead on the water.

So began a second terrible mourning period for Charlie. At night June could hear him crying for his mate. In the daytime he built and sat inside another stone nest, hoping that more chicks might appear. Everyone was at a loss as to what to do.

Finally a rabbit was put into his enclosure and the two animals became friends. Charlie stole the rabbit's carrots for his nest and, as soon as he relaxed, the rabbit took them back. It was company of a sort but each night Charlie called for his true mate. It was a sad situation but nothing could be done.

One evening June spotted a dog in the zoo. She rushed to catch it, fearing it would alarm the animals but could not do so before it had chased the fallow deer stag. Within a few minutes the stag dropped dead, a post mortem revealing that its heart had failed.

June was reminded yet again of the enormous responsibility towards the captive animals and vowed to help her parents in every way to ensure their well-being and safety. Much discussion about the welfare of the animals took place in the kitchen. One evening, much to everyone's amusement there was a new visitor. Rob-Rob, a large red and blue Macaw, walked in and flew to the back of June's chair, his fearsome beak skilfully lifting individual hairs from the back of her small neck and playing with them. No one took any notice. He turned his head on one side, listening to the noisy parrots, which had been brought in for the night. They were safely kept in one of the many bedrooms and June thought that maybe Rob-Rob wished to join them!

June loved to be in the kitchen garden at any time of the year. A short walk across the back yard of The Oakfield, surrounded by brick walls and sheltered from the elements, it was a paradise for a gardener intent on providing food for the family. Grandad could be spotted amongst the plants and vegetables, stopping occasionally to lean on his spade and smoke his pipe.

His granddaughter would skip along the path, entering the walled garden from the back yard of The Oakfield. She often peeped into the shed where the apples and pears were stored on shelves and the root vegetables were dug into the sand. The darkness and damp smell reminded her of winter. She would count the rows of fruit, bounty of the warm summer months, marvelling at this pantry of food so carefully stored.

Grandad's efforts provided security against the cold winter months, his consistency and knowledge of gardening turning the worked earth into a potential feast for both humans and animals at the zoo.

June would push past the beans, peas, lettuce, beetroot, tomatoes, cabbage and sprouts, making her way towards the two small wooden greenhouses. One provided tomatoes and cucumbers, which were used for the salads sold to the visitors.

She admired the espaliered apples which flattened and trained, grew along the three walls producing an abundance of fruit. Next to the greenhouses lay the vegetable garden and across the path were the bedding out flowers, which would be replanted into the flowerbeds in the zoo gardens.

June loved to squeeze and smell the mint leaves and inspect the fast growth of the rhubarb. She knew which greenhouse would contain her grandfather. She walked along the footpath, which ran close to the 10-foot wall. South facing, it supported the grape vines, peach and nectarine trees all of which had been pruned ready for spring growth.

The greenhouse she entered was special. She even spoke in a whisper when she spotted her grandfather bending over some plants at the far end. In that small area he grew flowers with a long name, a mysterious name that had evaded June until she was in the infant school.

'Auriculas'..... These flowers were grandad's passion. He grew them for shows, not just for local exhibitions but also for Grand National exhibits. Each year he made a long journey to London, to South Kensington where he judged auriculas from across Britain. Considered a great authority on such matters he was an honoured and knowledgeable guest.

Grandad's first visit to the great London Flower Show was made in 1881. Even when he came to live at Chester he continued to be invited to all the National flower shows as a judge. He was an expert in his field.

He also judged in the Northern Section of the Society in Manchester, pointing out the finest details required in the perfect auriculas. Grandad was a perfectionist, an incredible gardener, and from him June learnt how to grow and love plants. Because of her grandad's influence June's fingers were dabbling in the soil from when she first could walk. She loved gardening.

She also learnt the finer points of the auriculas, knowledge which would remain with her all of her life.

Grandad with bedding out plants

The Conservatory on the outside wall of the courtyard.
It was badly damaged by shrapnel from ack ack fire during
WW 2 and had to be demolished
(no 21 on the zoo map)

June with Sadie and Charlie (no 9 on zoo map)

10

'All because of the lions'

As spring approached the words 'garden party' were spoken by her father as he discussed finances with his wife. June dreaded those words, as it would mean fund raising, dressing up and being polite to even the most annoying visitors. Above all, it would mean hours and hours of preparation but her father was intent on raising money in order to establish a pride of lions. Eventually there would be a breeding programme and new housing would have to be built for the beasts. After all, every real zoo had lions. Later in the year, Lord Leverhulme would lay a foundation stone heralding the commencement of important and extensive works.

June realised that the zoo must always come first, had always come first, but from now on she would say what she thought. This gave her satisfaction as she prepared herself for the inevitable garden party. That evening she made her way to Punch's pen to inform him of the future event, the hard work, the efforts of her mother hidden away in the kitchen preparing food for the visitors, and about the plans for the new lion pen which had started all of this.

The great lonely bear heaved himself to his feet and padded across to his customary position, leaning against the side of his enclosure.

"If anyone is to have a new home then it should be you, Punch. You're stuck in there with just a pool of water inside that stinking little place. You arrived first and you should have the new home. All this garden party stuff should be for you, that's what I think," she whispered fiercely.

Punch exhaled hot reeking breath into her face. June loved him.

Everyone had to do as they were told for the safety and growth of their father's dream. Grimly, she resigned herself to the occasion; it was only a single day after all. It would be filled with hard work, of course, but she would help her mother all she could, serving teas, clearing away and even washing up at the end of the party.

71

There were many invitations given out including those to Council members; members of the North of England Zoological Society, and in particular Mrs Johnson who loaned the zoo money with which to purchase land. Benefactors, including the Russell-Allens and their friends and the Duke of Westminster and his guests who were keen to see the rehoused no longer free range capybara which he had donated. Invitations were given to the Marquis of Tavistock, Lord Leverhulme, friend and member of the zoo, Lady Daresbury, Miss Esther Holt and members of the shipping family.

A number of business people from Chester, donors of food for the zoo, were also invited. The list grew and grew. So did the cost but it was a mission that would eventually bring in the much-needed finance for the start of the new lion enclosure without bars.

The Mottershead household prepared for days, organising the food, the placing of the stalls and perfecting the spring gardens. It would be a much needed fund raiser for the lion enclosures and everyone must help. The fund raising day was to be held in May 1936. June was rehearsed for her speech to a titled lady who had accepted the invitation to open the fete. She had never visited the zoo before and as visitors began to pull into the grounds June shuffled her feet uncomfortably and waited to see the aristocratic lady.

She wondered just how many silly questions she would have to answer and of course the following day would entail hours of picking up paper bags and half eaten food, all this so that the lions could have an improved enclosure. But she was her father's daughter. She smiled brightly at the visitors, watched her father welcome everyone, saw the expensive car roll up and a tall, slim lady step out, waving to the chauffeur to park elsewhere.

Lady Delves Broughton was late, something which June's father did not encourage. But it appeared that with a Lady this did not matter. Mr Mott engaged her in polite conversation, which was soon interrupted by the return of the chauffeur carrying a pet gibbon. Lifting him into her arms, Lady Delves Broughton explained that her dear little Gibby had escaped and climbed the trees along the drive of Doddington Hall, Nantwich where they lived. Children began to gather around her as she stroked 'Miss Gibbs', pretending to chastise the naughty pet.

"You see, she is far too fond of birds' eggs, although I do not encourage her to eat them. I had such difficulty in securing her. She simply would not come down from the trees. Finally she did so and then we set off but we had such difficulty finding our way through the lanes of Cheshire. You are rather secluded here, right out in the countryside but nevertheless here we are!"

June stared at Lady Delves Broughton's expensive silk flowered dress, the beautifully cut navy blue coat and fine hat, and then at the long-armed gibbon pulling at her buttons.

"Such a dear little creature! I have only acquired her quite recently, just

a few months ago when I picked her up in London. Gibby loves travelling, don't you dear? Do you know she was just so well behaved on the train journey back to Crewe? For the entire journey she sat under my coat, very quiet and happy."
June stared at the slim aristocratic woman and wondered if it was the same person whose photographs had been in the local papers. Shown as the heroine of many a big game shoot and one of the finest tunny fishers in the world, she had won the admiration of many. It hardly seemed possible.

Clutching tightly to Miss Gibbs, Lady Delves Broughton made a short speech praising the efforts of Mr Mottershead and his efforts to place animals in an environment which resembled their natural state.

"I am all in favour of space for animals. They should not be kept confined and left to pace up and down in cages. I have seen the freedom that they have in Africa."

She smiled politely as a burst of applause drowned her next words.

"I declare the fête open and look forward to my guided tour around what appears to be a unique and fascinating zoological garden."

Mr Edis proposed a vote of thanks, adding hastily that funds were urgently needed if the zoo was to go ahead with future enclosures. Mr David, the bank manager, seconded that as Lady Delves Broughton nodded enthusiastically and the crowd clapped in agreement.

"I am sure that most of you know our charming visitor," he continued. "We are delighted to have our honoured guest here today and we have all read of her amazing achievements as a game hunter and amazing fisher."

The proposition for more funding was no longer in doubt. All that remained was for June to step forward and present a basket of lilac blooms to Lady Delves Broughton. A chameleon had been placed in the midst of the flowers. Quietly she wondered how long the reptile would last as Miss Gibbs spotted the creature immediately.

Trailing after the important entourage, June listened to her father expertly explaining his future plans to his important guest as she enthused over the open enclosures, the shrubberies and trees, the colourful banks of flowers and the smooth lawns.

June felt a sense of pride, for the gardens looked beautiful even though the day was cold and Mew had told her that only about three hundred people had turned up, far fewer than expected. She knew what that would mean. There would have to be another event for fund raising but right now she was determined to enjoy herself.

Leaving the main party, she wandered past the stalls, watching people purchasing goods and amusing themselves with the many competitions and games. Dr Moulden waved at her, calling her over to try her luck on the sliding penny stall, which he was in charge of. A little girl rushed past her, dragging her mother along by the hand.

"Look Mummy, a tortoise for 1/6, but I want the big one for five shillings."

Someone had lined two tortoises up for a race but they were so cold that they retreated wisely into their shells, one climbing on top of the other. There was much laughter at this.

"They are so disgusted they refuse to race," laughed the girl's father, as June thought to herself, 'Can't you work it out that they have just come out of hibernation?'

For most of the afternoon she wandered round the stalls. The bowling was boring but the hoopla and coconut shies were fun. Crowds of spectators gathered around the pig guessing stall, small children fished for bottles, jumped on beanbags and joined in the balloon race, which Mrs Grousell had organised. Everyone June knew seemed to be trying to make the day a success.

She could hear music being played. The Chester hospital band was in full flow near the area around The Oakfield where teas were being served to visitors. That reminded June that soon she would be washing up hundreds of dishes, and she dragged her feet. She didn't enjoy that job.

Several visitors had won competitions and carried their prizes home with them, beautifully coloured birds in small cages. June smiled to herself. The fund-raising seeds had been sown.

People began to leave as the shadows lengthened across the lawns. June sat on the steps of The Oakfield watching her father talking enthusiastically with his secretary, too enthusiastically! So she wandered inside to watch her mother working efficiently with eleven helpers, organised and dedicated. Mrs Mott never raised her voice, never wore an apron, but remained immaculate and toiled unstintingly.

Mew came in looking flustered.

"What's wrong, Mew?" June questioned, feeling guilty, as she had done so little.

"Where's Dad? The temperature has dropped and I need to turn up the heating for the chimps. A couple of them are snuffling. I will have to interrupt his socialising. The animals come first, that is what he is always telling us, isn't it?"

June knew immediately that Mew was in a very bad mood. She had attended to the animals all afternoon, avoiding the visitors.

"Oh yes, I think I know where he is – impressing his girlfriends, no doubt," and she stormed out.

June thought about that for a moment. She turned her head and watched her mother calmly going about her work. She thought about her father socialising on the lawn. She decided that Mew was simply in a bad temper and she'd keep out of her way for a while.

Later the dancing started, the lawns lit up by candles and oil lamps.

While her father danced with his guests, June's mother remained in the kitchen and June began again to think about Mew's words.

Determined to find out, she set off down the paths to find her sister.

Soon she was at the chimp house where she saw Mew's dark shape in the enclosure.

"Oh, it's you, June. Hold this chimp, please. She is still suffering from that awful seasickness and now she has a cold. I think we will take her inside for the night."

"Mew, what is wrong with Dad? You seem so angry."

Mew remained silent for a moment, and then replied. "Sometimes I feel sorry for Mum. She works so hard. In a minute she will be down here checking all the animals, never misses you know, and Dad is always with other women. Nothing new, June! He's always done it. Mum is his wife, so don't worry about it. He isn't going anywhere but I just feel sorry for . . ."

She straightened up and strode purposefully out of the chimp house. June ran after her, holding the little chimp against her chest.

"But Mew?"

"No more!" her sister responded curtly. "Now come around the back through the courtyard. I don't want to be spotted by the visitors looking like this. Go and find Charlie. He's helping grandad. Make yourself useful June. Tomorrow we will have to clean up the mess from the human zoo."

She disappeared inside the house.

The following day it rained but the grounds had to be cleaned up, the half eaten sandwiches and rubbish collected, and chairs and stalls dismantled. That evening at supper Mr Mott talked about the next big fund raiser, which would take place in July. The Conservative Party had approached him over the use of the grounds for their fete.

They would organise all activities, leaving only refreshments and catering to the Mottershead family. Not only would they pay for the use of the twenty-acre grounds but would attract sponsorship and interest. It was the perfect chance to raise money towards the lion enclosure. Sir Charles Cayzer, Member of Parliament, would make a speech although there would be no official opening ceremony. The occasion was intended to offset the effect of a Liberal fête, which had taken place elsewhere in the district.

Preparations began well in advance, various stalls and side shows lining the avenue to the house which, they were quick to point out, had once belonged to the late Mr B. C. Roberts, former Chairman of the party. It would be the perfect setting for the fete.

Four thousand people were expected to attend from Chester and the surrounding countryside areas. The car park was made available and visitors streamed in by the thousands. The zoological grounds were totally transformed for the event.

On the main lawn in front of the house were an acrobatic troupe and morris dancers. Public dancing would take place in the evening. On the fringe of the lawn was placed a funfair and sideshows were arranged at various points throughout the grounds.

In an adjacent field a clay pigeon shoot attracted a large entry and many competitions, such as darts and shooting, were available. The weather was fine and warm, the Conservative Party members feeling that the luck of the Conservative Party still held in Chester, as in general the weather had been appalling.

June joined the crowds of people as they wandered about the gardens, listening with pride as they commented on the rose beds, the flowers showing up brilliantly against the background of shrubbery. Thousands of people sat under the trees in the shade and music drifted from the lawns of The Oakfield.

Children laughed at the monkeys that scampered up the trees, eating bananas and any food that good-natured spectators gave to them. Two old ladies enjoyed watching the grizzly bear, calling out to him and requesting him to roll over. He refused, as he was too hot; he simply lay down, grunted and ate the food nearest to him.

At 4.00 pm precisely the Morris dancers in their short yellow frocks performed to a large standing audience. They clicked the white-streamered Morris sticks, faultless with their well-rehearsed routine.
June wandered past the ever-popular palmist tent, pausing to peep inside. She had often wondered about being able to look into the future. Was it possible to know what might happen? Certainly she could never predict from day to day just what might occur in her zoo.

The closing speech was held on the lawn. The Directors of the zoo were thanked and it was suggested that to repay the debt for the delightful venue people could become members or fellows of the North of England Zoological Society.

Social reforms were spoken of, for the government had passed a bill which gave unemployment insurance to agricultural labourers. Only the previous day, the final stages of the Midwives' Bill had been completed, setting up a midwifery service throughout the country. June understood none of this, but as she stood amongst the crowds, a small anonymous girl, she knew with certainty that her father was a great man for he had created something unique. Her parents believed in a dream and in doing so they had made it happen. The animals of the world were finding their way to Chester Zoo because people had begun to believe in the Mottershead vision.

Far away on the Atlantic Ocean a travelling zoo was making its way to Chester. The vessel, named the *Robert Holt*, was sailing from the Cameroons to England in 1936.

On board were two caged leopards, nearly twelve months old; two palm rats; a palm civet; two monitor lizards; seven crocodiles; and a drill baboon. Mr Darwell, the company's agent and the Vice Consul at Duala, had presented them to the zoo.

Pandemonium had broken loose on the ship at one point, as the drill baboon had escaped. Initially it had made friends with the crewmembers and enjoyed walks on the deck, tethered by a rope, but one evening it escaped from its guardian, sneaking off to visit the monitor lizards. Craftily, the monkey slipped the catch on their cage. An hour later a native seaman ran to the Captain. He was very agitated.

"Come sir, quick," he gasped. "Thing under winch, it come and go like that."

To explain what he meant the man shot his arm backward and forward like a piston. A scouting party discovered that it was the sizeable lizard, which resenting the interruption to its unchecked walk around the ship, and was spitting out its alarming tongue.

A seaman who had been advised to wear thick leather gauntlet gloves tried to catch the lizard. It had other ideas. It snapped its teeth, biting through the thick leather of the gloves. It finished off the attack with a lash of its tail, cutting clean through the glove and scarring the seaman's arm.

The leopards, which hated both light and people, slept on, snoring from the depths of their cage. Only at night did they wake to pace restlessly up and down, stopping briefly to consume the proffered meat.

The fascinating destiny and legends of the zoo without bars had spread far beyond England.

Muriel serving teas on the lawn

Punch

LADY BROUGHTON, with "Miss Gibbs," her pet Siamese gibbon, which she brought back from her travels this spring, on her arrival at Chester Zoo, Upton, Cheshire, to open a Country Fair and Fête in aid of the North of England Zoological Society.

The fete

11

'There was an old woman
Who lived in a shoe,
She had so many children
She sent them to the zoo'

On a warm August day in 1937 three Crossville buses set out from The People's Hall, Delamere Street, Chester in the direction of Chester Zoo. On board were over sixty children and adults, on an outing provided by the Chester Unemployed Association.

They carried with them packages of food wrapped in brown paper, bottles of milk, cases of lemonade and dozens of oranges. The buses took them through the Cheshire lanes, deep into the countryside. As they peered through the windows they caught glimpses of hedgerows brimming with flowers, greenery replacing the dark streets and alleyways of their city life.

The excitement had been brimming for days, ever since they had discovered that this year's excursion was to be to a zoo. Some of the people had turned up a day early in their enthusiasm to see the animals!

The previous year they had been taken up the river to Eaton and played in three fields on the Duke of Westminster's estate. This time it was to be a visit to Chester Zoo at Upton. Some of the children boasted prior knowledge of zoos because they had made previous visits. Many of the children had never seen live animals from foreign countries, only knowing of them from picture books and through geography lessons and textbooks. One small girl was sick into a paper bag at the thought of seeing such exotic wildlife and had to be consoled.

Upon their arrival they rushed around the zoo, anxiously watched by parents and helpers. The small girl who had been so anxious immediately leapt onto a wall and almost fell onto two small black bears. She was saved by her parents and quickly led off to see the fallow deer, a native animal of Britain.

A little boy thought the antlers of the deer would be ideal to hang his hat on!

At the monkey house they fed the animals with lettuce and cabbage leaves, laughing with delight as the monkeys chattered, responding to their small visitors. One chimp grabbed a boy's hat and ran about with it on its head.

Groups of children gathered round George the parrot who allowed them to stroke his feathers, shouting out "Hello" each time a child approached him. They saw birds from all over the world, coloured fish in their tanks and a towering dirty-looking polar bear which stared silently at them.

One of the mothers, Mrs Bolter, carried a baby in her arms as her four sons, Ernie, Jonnie, Ronnie and Kennie, rushed around enjoying themselves. She was so happy but wished her thirteen year old daughter, busy working at a menial job, could have come on the trip too.

Children scattered in every direction, running about under the trees, playing hide and seek and finally trooping back to the trestle table which was laden with sandwiches and cakes. By 4.30pm, exhausted, hungry and happy, they ate the food washed down with lemonade or milk.

They chattered about their experiences in 'the jungles of Africa', and then sang a silly song at the top of their voices:

'There was an old woman who lived in a shoe,
she had so many children she sent them to the zoo'.

Stomachs were full and, as their energy returned, they clambered up to play cricket, rounders and racing for prizes. Finally, exhausted, they lay about on the grass swapping stories of daring deeds, imagination carrying them to the furthest corners of the earth.

At 7 o'clock it was time to go home. The buses sounded their horns as a signal to board and they begrudgingly left the magical place in the heart of the countryside in exchange for their city life. Mr Mott and his eleven-year-old daughter June waved to them as they boarded the buses, one little girl suddenly breaking down and crying as, for some inexplicable reason, she wished to stay with the animals.

June and her father waved goodbye, returning home through the turnstile. No words were spoken for there was no need.

The zoo acquired more land containing an oak tree and a cow shed. This was soon made into a home for a Malayan bear named Sally. Her owner could no longer handle her, as she had grown too large and she became a donation to the zoo. A circular wall and ditch were built around the oak tree, part of the cowshed became an indoor pen and Sally was moved into it. This was the first open enclosure built in the zoo and the staff christened the site "Whipsnade."

Sally was joined by a mate, bought for that purpose, and they quickly grew used to climbing the tree, eventually turning it into a skeletal and leafless trunk as they broke all the branches. Part of the cowshed was fenced off for a stable occupied by a llama that grazed on the remainder of the land. Mr Mott never refused to take an animal; there was a welcome home for all living creatures.

Finally the day arrived when Lord Leverhulme officially laid the foundation stone, October the nineteenth 1937. This busy and important day began with a typical autumnal dawn, when animals were attended to and last minute preparations were made for the official visitors.

As the morning progressed, June sensed the excitement in her father, as he appeared in a smart suit, ready to welcome the guests. Her mother was working steadily in the kitchen as usual, adding the finishing touches to the tea which would follow the speeches.

Mew had vanished into the monkey enclosure to clean it out, Charlie was helping and Grandad tidied the fallen leaves from the driveway and paths. Everyone was quietly busy and preoccupied. June slipped away to talk with Punch, explaining to him that one day he too would enjoy a new enclosure. Mr Mott explained that the laying of the foundation stone would be the start to the outdoor enclosure for the lions. There were plans for artificial sunlight, which would be beamed down from sun lamps, central heating would warm the indoor areas and extra radiators would give more heating on chilly nights. The long hoped for enclosure would represent a miniature jungle. The holly and yew trees were to be been rooted up and removed in case of scratches to the lions.

June looked around, remembering the wilderness of garden, the fox hunting that took place across the land when they first moved there, and the zoo in her head which was transforming itself into reality. It was her world and she had begun to realise that it was like no other place on earth. It was different, she was different, and no wonder she felt that no one in her class could possibly understand what was happening here.

Cars were arriving, her father was shaking hands and smiling and June stood back, looking across her garden to the shrubberies and small area of wilderness that remained. Another 'zoo' lived in there, she decided. Hedgehog trails and small animal paths retreated into the tangle of brambles. She knew of the foxes that had made their den deep in the undergrowth, and rabbit droppings betrayed the food source of the wilderness. A wild owl flew low over The Oakfield at dusk; sometimes she had followed his silent flight as, like some giant moth, he had momentarily hovered over a vole or mouse before his nightly feed.

In the aviary the captive owls sat still on their branch perches, their diet consisting mainly of horsemeat with an occasional dead mouse for roughage. She had broken open an owl pellet during one of her walks into the wood, astonished to discover the tiny bones and fur of unknown creatures.

Yet again she questioned the meaning of the zoo in which her father's dream persisted and grew despite the ever-growing demand for finances. His ambition had brought floating arks to England, removing creatures from their freedom only to struggle to give back some of that freedom. June puzzled over this. It was her personal and private dilemma and so far she had found no satisfactory answer.

She hurried along the paths to join the group of dignitaries. Lord Leverhulme's speech had commenced.

"I have officially attended many openings but the laying of this foundation stone is a unique experience."

June smiled as Mary the chimp beat the ground with her feet, angry at not being allowed to mix freely with the guests.

"Plans are to build a wall, from twelve to eighteen feet high, around the enclosure, surmounting it with terraces so that visitors can watch the prowling lions in a natural environment."

A shriek from one of the official party brought the speech to a stop. Pelly the pelican had grabbed a man's trilby hat from behind as he had inadvertently leaned against her pen. One of the keepers hurried over and released it from a grinning Pelly.

"As I was about to say, it will be a big improvement on the Whipsnade Zoo as the lions can still be watched by the public if they enter the indoor lion house for warmth."

The noise of a coin hitting the ground caused June to look up. Flying low overhead was the rogue magpie, heading for his secret collection of all things shiny, including money and rings. June and Charlie knew where his hoard of wealth lay stored but it was his secret.

"The zoo now has three fully grown lionesses."

As if on cue, their roaring emphasised the subject of his speech, ferocious primeval sounds which caused a few visitors to shudder.

June felt bored, wandering off to check on Mary. She stood in a corner of her pen looking gloomy. It was conker time and some children had been feeding the animals with juicy brown horse chestnuts. June wondered if Mary had eaten some of them and made herself ill. Maybe she was sulking as she was fastened up. Mary was extremely gentle, usually following all the family around in and out of the house.

Mary's performance over the last few weeks, helping Mr Mott with the laying of the bricks on the cement, and lifting the wood for the foundations of the new indoor lion pen, had been quite amazing. By this time she was a very large chimp, heavier than June and capable of all kinds of mischief. But she was extremely intelligent, consistently well behaved, so was allowed free range of the zoo. Not today for some strange reason!

Nearer to the main gate the Malayan bears were very busy in their enclosure, stripping the leaves from the large oak. Pigeon-toed and long clawed, in their natural state they looked for honey; now they were accelerating the effect of autumn.

Glancing back, June watched the visitors as they moved slowly away from the site of the foundation stone next to the penguin enclosure. Formalities were at an end. The guests joined her father to look more closely at the lions. June joined them, moving nearer to the lion cage.

Lord Leverhulme stood within a foot of the three young lionesses, Faith, Hope and Charity. They curled their lips, snarling and pacing. He poked a hand through the bars of their temporary cages and quickly withdrew it, this token gesture causing much amusement amongst the guests. He glanced appreciatively at the China Doulton figure of a lion that had been presented to him by Miss Russell Allen.

Mr Narrowmore proposed a final vote of thanks, adding that he hoped his Lordship had had some little sport that afternoon in the lion house and he trusted that when the enclosure was complete he would 'venture to have a day's sport in the jungle'.

Amidst much laughter the party moved slowly off towards The Oakfield and June went in the opposite direction trying to puzzle out why everyone had laughed. Unfortunately the outdoor lion pen enclosure would not be built until after the war.

The laying of the foundation stone was a turning point for the zoo. Well publicised, and later praised by visitors and through newspaper reports, it signalled a huge step towards recognition of a growing national zoo. With the publicity came even more animals, exotic species from lands far away, including exchanges from other zoos such as Bristol and Whipsnade and local contributions from the public who offered their unusual 'pets' that they could no longer look after.

In October there was a unique birth at the zoo that created much excitement in the zoo world. A baby mandrill was born, the first one to be born in captivity. She was named Dawn. A tiny creature with large eyes, she snuggled for protection into her mother's breast. She appeared to be a lusty baby and soon became the subject of requests for many photographs. Mandrills, a large type of baboon, are extremely fierce in the wild, George Mottershead patiently explained to reporters who had requested photographs of Dawn being held by a keeper. For her to survive, total respect and privacy needed to be given the family, and with that the photo session came to an end.

But for some unaccountable reason Dawn's mother began to pluck out Dawn's eyebrows and the hair on her forehead, leaving the young animal almost bald. This behaviour continued for weeks until finally she left her baby alone.

Mew laughed about the young mandrill's father named George and his enforced isolation from the new baby. He was removed because he was extremely selfish and would take all the extra food and delicacies intended for the baby.

George and his mate had arrived two years before from West Africa, his bad behaviour and greedy manner apparent from the time he entered the zoo.

Now all he could see of the new baby was from his isolated position. He was in a very black mood as he watched all the attention heaped on Dawn.

"Animals show very human traits," Mew commented dryly to June as they looked at the baby through the wire of their enclosure.

That evening June's father relaxed after their evening meal in the kitchen, pleased that positive signs of real progress were occurring.

"In answering complaints about cruelty to enclosed animals, there is a humanitarian article in the paper," he smiled. "Listen to this bit: 'Motorists can use the free car park. When I went there I passed under an arch surmounted by a lucky horseshoe'. That was father's idea and it's proved a good one."

"Go on, George! Read some more to us. It's pleasing to hear that we are gaining support."

Elizabeth sat back in her chair and Mew and June listened attentively.

'I met George Mottershead. He was dressed for hard work. He is practical, not just thinking and planning.'

Mr Mott turned to his family, laying down the paper for a moment.

"You see, I have always said that appearances matter. We have to be seen to be doing . . ."

"Doing what, George? Hard work? It's all hard work. I worry about how we are to feed the animals. More arrive every day."

Lizzie, ever practical, sighed, thinking about yet another consignment of creatures heading in their direction from West Africa.

Picking up the paper, Mr Mott continued. 'In the entrance hall to the large manor is a model of the new open lion enclosure. Mr Mottershead feels that lions need something to play with and has provided his lions with large wooden toys'.

'The zoo is very clean and roomy. I saw a beautiful pelican, which had sought its freedom when being brought by ship to England. It was explained to me that the captain of the ship sent his log record to the zoo. The bird was eventually captured by lifeboat but it took hours.'

"Here's a piece about you, June... 'The black-footed penguins were secluded because of moulting but Billy the goat was paying 'copycat' with June Mottershead, aged eleven."

"Yes, Dad, I remember the man taking a photograph of me head-to-head with Billy...."

"Another picture!" she muttered under her breath.

Her father continued, immensely pleased by the article ".... 'Adults pay one shilling. Children pay sixpence.'.... Do you think we need to consider raising the entrance cost?"

Everyone emphatically nodded in agreement, and George went on " 'I saw the beautiful fallow deer and Himalayan sun bears playing in the open air with a huge tree in the centre of their enclosure. This is supposed to be the only enclosure of its kind'."

Mr Mott paused to sip his tea. There was an air of expectation in the room.

Mew added fuel to the fire, as the air was growing chilly. Mr Mott cleared his throat and continued.

'The Chief Justice of Nigeria, Sir Donald Kingdon, has presented seven Senegal parakeets, West African doves and some touracos from the Gold Coast and a hill myna which talks better than a parrot.'

He stopped reading, scrutinising the next part of the newspaper article.

"What is it, Dad?" June asked, seeing a change in her father's expression.

"Well, here's something we must change, I'm afraid. He thinks the signs around the zoo need replacing and is suggesting that someone might help. He's right. They are shabby but at the moment that is the least of our concerns."

'A zoological library is steadily being assembled and the staff live comfortably in the mansion.'

"Not as comfortably as the lions", June thought. "I am still freezing in bed and Charlie has started sleeping in his socks and wearing a hat! And it's not even winter yet."

George Mottershead was in full swing now, jubilant at the contents of the article.

'Exotic fish in grottos, housed in electrically illuminated glass tanks, will eventually be moved under the house. Alligators and crocodiles are kept in a pool – they are all still quite small but will become dangerous as they grow older.'

"Where will we put them then, Dad?" Mew enquired.

"We will consider that later, Mew", her father reassured her. "Everything in due time."

"A sanctuary for wild birds is located in the orchard. There are many rare and beautiful birds of prey. Canadian black bears and the Indian and African pythons are . . ."

June heard no more as she slid into a warm and comfortable sleep, happy and secure within her human and animal family. Her blossoming zoo appeared to be safe. Nothing else mattered.

Winter was fast approaching. Out in the countryside of Cheshire nature was in retreat. The last of the wild flowers rotted down by rain disappeared from the lanes; the mystery of thick ancient woods was stripped bare by the piercing November winds, exposed and naked. Rooks called from the tops of these skeletal trees and the first frosts arrived, skimming the ponds with thin, treacherous sheets of ice.

The wealthy headed for warmer climates, and the villagers withdrew for the winter into their cottages and small tight communities. Fewer and fewer visitors visited Chester Zoo. The takings shrank and the animals needed constant feeding, but nothing deterred the Mottershead family as they awoke in their chilly mansion, knowing how busy would be the day that lay ahead for each of them.

Mary the chimp helping Mr Mottershead to build the indoor lion enclosures (no 4 on zoo map)

Lord Leverhulme laying the foundation stone
for the outside lion enclosure - 1937
L- R Mr Narrowmore, Miss Russell Allen, Mr Grousell, Chairman of NEZS
Mr Dixon, Mr Mottershead, Charlie Collins, Lord & Lady Leverhulme

12

'All things bright and beautiful'

Bonfire night! No one needed reminding of this echo of barbarism – an exciting annual event when all over Britain there would be a frenzy of bonfire building and other activities leading up to the lighting of the fires.

"Penny for the Guy?" was the cry from many a street corner and in doorways as groups of children dragged around straw-filled effigies of a man representing the infamous Guy Fawkes who had tried, but failed, to blow up the Houses of Parliament in 1605.

Great heaps of wood and old furniture appeared on waste ground and on allotments weeks before the traditional burning. Several of them were deliberately lit beforehand in an attempt to evoke a thrilling but potentially dangerous adventure for the children.

The same children who had sneaked up and lit other bonfires jealously guarded their own patch, as the wood grew higher. Finally, the Guy was placed on the top where he remained, bulbously padded or sticklike, maybe wearing a battered top hat or a bonnet.

Mothers made biscuits, cakes and slabs of treacle toffee. Sacks of potatoes stood in back yards ready for throwing into the dying embers of the fire, to be poked out and eaten, tasting of charcoal and smoke. Fathers added last minute alterations to the stacking of support wood whilst children gathered round in admiration, for this annual event, although somewhat redolent of primitiveness, had the stamp of adult approval.

The first winter frosts had arrived, turning the lawns into silver, ice white beneath a moon that hung in the velvet sky like an ill omen. June and her sister Mew were out checking each enclosure as dark fell, their shoes wet with heavy frost, their finger tips and noses icy. June trotted at her sister's side, trying to keep up with Mew's urgent pace. The faint scent of distant bonfires hung in the air.

Mew was dressed in an old hat and long black coat and she carried a stick, which she used every so often to thrust into the undergrowth. They searched for one of the peacocks that had an injured foot. Unable to fly into the trees and roost, the bird needed to be caught and taken into the sanctuary of The Oakfield.

" All things bright and beautiful,
All creatures great and small,
All things wise and wonderful,
The Lord God made them all "

June's voice rang out as she remembered the words from the school assembly that week. Loudly, defiantly, she repeated the verse as she ran after the dark figure striding out in front of her.

It had the desired effect. Mew whirled round. "Shut up, June. What's wrong with you? Why are you singing that silly hymn, frightening everything?"

June trailed behind, silent. She had just wanted to communicate and break the tense atmosphere, that was all. Their feet crunched on the frosty paths. In defiance she sang the words in her head, and then she hummed the tune.

Mew stopped again. "June, why are you trying to irritate me? Go back to the house if you can't shut up. Anyway, think about the words; I don't think you know what you are singing."

Over and over in her head June repeated the words. She slowed down and stood still for a second. Her sister disappeared into the night. Yes, Mew was right. The words were silly. All things were definitely not bright and beautiful. She thought of Punch and grinned to herself. And animals were not necessarily wise, they learnt to be canny in order to survive or they died. And the last line?

Suddenly she knew the answer to that. The animals recreated themselves. No one made them with some kind of magic wand. She was eleven years of age but she had observed their breeding, their deaths and their struggle for survival. She knew that only the fittest and the strongest survived, even with help from the family. Out there on the polar ice or in the wild forests their fate might be decided in an instant.

She wouldn't sing the hymn ever again.

They reached the great cedar near to The Oakfield, the lights from the house outlining the closed shapes of the peacocks' hanging tails as they perched high on the branches. Several of them fluttered down into the blackness, strutting across the frosty lawn.

"Fly up," pleaded June, running towards them, clapping her hands so that they all fluttered away into the bushes.

The door of The Oakfield opened, a flood of light trickling down the steps and spilling onto the lawn. She could see the outline of her mother.

"June, come in right now. It's your bedtime."

The following morning a tell-tale display of peacock feathers, bright

90

green and blue 'eyes', lay strewn on the path beyond the monkey enclosure, revealing the fate of the peacocks.

June Mottershead had taken her first steps towards grappling with Spencer's 'survival of the fittest' notion and opening the door to the evolution of species concept, which was a contentious issue in the world around her.

On December the seventeenth, a pair of waterbuck arrived in Liverpool. Immediately they were sent into quarantine owing to the Ministry of Agriculture's restriction on the import of animals suspected of foot and mouth disease.

On December the twenty second, a further consignment of specimens for the zoo arrived at Portland. It consisted of a pair of mandrills and a black-crested eagle. The zoo was growing at an alarming rate. More funds were needed as soon as possible.

June now had a new and important role. On most evenings she sat at a large office desk in one of the many bedrooms and folded single sheets of typewritten paper that had been run off on a duplicating machine.

1937 was the beginning of 'Our Zoo News', which was sold at the pay box and in the café. Members and friends of the zoo had it sent to them by post. Another 'family' of people was forming, lovers of the animals and faithful to the particular animal that they cared most about.

During the cold weeks of winter they turned up regularly to talk to the animals, bringing with them suitable titbits. A sulphur-crested cockatoo spoke to his human friend as she leaned towards him, reassuring him and feeding him all the little pieces of food that he loved.

Another lady accompanied by an old aunt collected syrup tins and brought them to the Malayan bears to lick out, perhaps evoking vanished times of honey eating in their jungle home. Miss Newstead from the Spinney visited the zoo every Christmas Day as it was so quiet. The zoo stayed open during Christmas but it was a quiet time for the Mottershead family, as most of the staff celebrated the special days with their families.

June knew that her Christmas was not like that of other children. It was business as usual but her mother tried to make up for the fact that there were no celebrations. She bought June presents including a bicycle, which she could ride around the zoo.

Grandad always carried in the Norfolk pine, which grew in the conservatory all the year round. It was used annually for June's Christmas tree, each year growing a little taller. June made paper chains and decorated it enthusiastically.

On Christmas morning she awoke early, searching with her toes for something heavy at the end of the bed. Yes, there it was, a pillowcase stuffed with presents. Many were predictable, which was in a strange way very reassuring.

Four years ago there was a teddy bear that she'd promptly tucked into bed with her. Later she trimmed him because she felt that by nature he would moult as the bears did in her zoo. He was still her treasured possession. June valued her presents, as she knew they were hard come by. This year there was an illustrated atlas that would be used to trace the journeys of the floating arks, until it eventually fell to pieces. A bag of chocolate coins, a tangerine and a new penny were at the bottom of her Christmas sack.

Curled up in bed, by the light of a candle she explored the new atlas, tracing the route that Punch must have made from his original icy land to England – never to return, she thought ruefully, and if he did he was far too dirty to sit out on the ice, camouflaged in the snow.

Then she examined Africa, which appeared to be covered in red. She'd always thought of it as one country but that morning brought new knowledge. It was made up of many countries and was called a continent. She looked intently at the atlas wondering where their enormous skull of a giant gorilla had come from. It had arrived in a wooden box, a present from a famous African chief, and initially it had frightened June. She reasoned that it was quite a natural thing as there must be many animal skulls in the wasteland near to the wood beyond the gardens. This was where all their dead animals were buried and would, in the words of her father, 'turn to dust'.

Later, this skull went into the growing artefact section of the zoo, ready to be placed in the educational centre which had yet to be built. She wondered if the gorilla had died from old age but intuition told her that he had been killed, maybe in order to steal baby gorillas. She recalled the baby monkeys that had arrived a few months ago and their struggle to survive.

As soon as it was light June was out of bed and quickly dressed. She came down to the kitchen to discover her mother already preparing the Christmas dinner. Granny traditionally made the Christmas pudding, boiled for hours in the Lodge laundry. Inside the outhouse of the Lodge stood a huge copper boiler beneath which a coal fire burned to heat the water and this was the birthplace of the traditional family Christmas pudding. June loved to eat it, longing to taste the rich fruit and secretly hoping to bite on a threepenny bit. Granny always hid several of these in the pudding but last year Charlie had discovered two of them, Mew one and June none at all.

So Christmas Day was enjoyed with the animals. Her father brought Mary into the house; Minnie snuffled outside the kitchen door; the usual hangers-on lined up for titbits or wandered into the kitchen, including a parakeet that repeatedly flew up onto the wooden table only to be shooed away. Parrots called out to each other from the upstairs bedroom where they had been taken to escape the harsh December wind and several hibernating tortoises were in cardboard boxes in the hallway.

From the grounds came the call of the peacocks and the roaring and snarling of the lions as they ripped into their daily ration of horsemeat. Every scratching noise, thump, squeal or growl was recognised by the family. Mew came in nursing a baby chimp, which was cuddling up to her for warmth.

Such was Christmas Day at Chester Zoo.

As darkness fell by 4.00 pm that afternoon, her joy was for the animals, fed and warm in their indoor enclosures. She was at home with her family, enjoying a special Christmas dinner. What more could she wish for?

Outside, the friendly wild owl hooted and the enclosed owls answered him, foxes lay deep in their labyrinthine den, and the birds huddled together for warmth in the foliage that covered both The Oakfield and the Lodge. Darkness and silence eventually covered the winter zoo. No light shone. June snuggled under the blankets in her bed, searching for her blue hot-water bottle for warmth and comfort.

Every winter she remembered the rheumatic malady she had suffered when she was six years of age. The excruciating and immediate pain was something she recalled in her later years. Brought on by the dampness of the great house, it had attacked her limbs until she could barely walk. Now she could hardly recall how she recovered from it but she still had strong memories of the pain when the wind howled and rain beat on the glass of The Oakfield.

When she was about five or six she also suffered from prolonged nosebleeds that had left her weak and miserable. They stopped when the weather became warmer and now they had ceased altogether.

There were no curtains at her bedroom windows and many times she sat up in her bed staring at the blackness, thinking of the dreaming lions, Punch curled up in his winter coat and of the many exotic creatures which made up her world.

Christmas passed and it was the daily round of work as usual for the Mottersheads. June knew of no other childhood, only fleetingly perceiving the differences when she visited friends' homes.

Only recently some additional land had been acquired by the society. A car park was made near to the Lodge and then another strip of land was purchased, part of a field adjoining the zoo where bungalows were about to be built.

Early in the New Year June's father warned the family and keepers about turning their backs on any animal, even for a second. It could mean certain death and he wanted no complacency. The Malayan bears were put into their new enclosure, situated on the land that had been recently purchased by the zoo. Part of the cattle shed that was on this land became the bears' indoor pen. Unfortunately the bears refused to go into it, leaving their keepers wide open to danger when they needed to clean both pens out. The men placed a ladder against the wall, keeping their ears and eyes open so that the bears did not sneak up on them whilst they were cleaning. If there were any sound of claws on the concrete, the keepers would turn and face the bears, showing them the brooms in their hands. The animals would then wander off.

One silly mistake or a moment of forgetfulness could be fatal, and such a warning could never be forgotten. Any thoughtless, cruel or inadequate keeper was asked to leave, as was one man who was discovered drinking the milk meant for the chimpanzees.

The Holt family visited the zoo often and were very generous in their support. One weekend early in spring June was working behind the counter of the little shop inside The Oakfield when Mr Holt pressed a ten-shilling note into her hand, telling her that it was wages for a hard-working girl. It was more than Mew earned in an entire week and June saved it for a very long time.

Mew passed by the counter on her way out to check on the chimps. The weather was still icy, the sharp wind was blowing into the pens and the chimps would be the first to catch colds and influenza. Mew hated this time of year; only through her persistence and perseverance did so many chimps survive their first winter in Chester Zoo, especially when the cold weather extended into spring

"Come and look at a very homesick little monkey, June," she called out as she rushed by.

Quickly June followed her, gasping as the cold wind bit into her clothes. Mew was going at her usual fast pace, making it hard for June to catch up. Finally she reached her sister's side and breathlessly she asked about the monkey.

"You remember, June, when Mrs Bailey of Horley Manor at Banbury gave us her pet monkey?"

"Wasn't that the one which kept clinging to her? Dad said afterwards that it is wrong to grow too close to an animal as you become its family, then it can't mix. Is that the one?"

"Yes. Well, Dad was right. I have never seen a monkey so sad and miserable .... Really homesick! Look, here it is, clinging to the wire!"

June looked down at a fully-grown woolly monkey with its long tail wrapped around its body. It was called 'the monkey with the fifth hand' because its powerful tail was used like a hand, which could be used to swing nimbly through the trees, especially in the wild.

The animal was quite large with thick hair, dark grey in colour. June had never seen Mew take it into the house yet, and clearly sensing the two watching girls, the monkey clung even more desperately to the wire. Mew knelt down and spoke softly but it buried its head in its hands in despair.

"Oh, Mew, it is homesick. How awful. What can we do?"

Suddenly the monkey started to sob, loudly and desperately, holding its hands over its face in anguish, so much like a little person, yet the girls could do nothing.

"June, run back to the house and tell Mum. She will know what to do, and whilst you are there get some little pieces of fruit. We will try and comfort it with titbits."

Soon the entire family were gathered around the pen. The monkey continued to cry, the wind blew icy rain onto them and June shivered.

Her father was decisive.

"No point bringing it into the house. You have never handled it, Mew, and you are not its family. Mrs Bailey is, and that's the trouble. What have I said about making animals dependent on humans? It isn't natural and this is the result!"

He was clearly upset but June knew that he was right. Now the monkey must take its chance. All of this time Mew was speaking softly to it and slowly the sobbing ceased. A little hand came through the bar and took a small piece of apple. June smiled. Her sister was so good with the chimps and monkeys.

"Come back into the house, Lizzie."

Mr Mott spoke quietly. He knew they were all upset but nothing could be done. The indoor area of the monkey enclosure was artificially heated. Maybe it would decide to seek comfort in there next to the chimpanzees, which were watching the entire event with great interest.

"I think it will survive. It has company and good living conditions."

Mr Mott spoke convincingly and June believed him. Within four days the sadness had gone and the woolly monkey had begun to share its life with the chimps. Mew kept a close eye on it for weeks but it never cried again, much to everyone's relief.

Mary the chimp loved her freedom but she was not the only one. Komo, a black-faced chimp, grew very strong, proving this by pushing the wire until it gave way. Tarzan, her mate, would twist and turn the screws until they became loose. Mary sounded the alarm that brought the two girls running to the courtyard. Finally their father built a strong pen next to their original one, knocked a hole in the wall between the two pens and gave a lump hammer to Komo and Tarzan. They took turns at enlarging it so that they could reach the new pen. Then the hole was blocked up, leaving them secure but with the psychological advantage of having 'discovered' their new home.

June sensed the huge responsibility which went with this extended animal family, especially as it was growing every day. Grateful, and relieved by the strength her father showed in emergencies, she lay in bed that night questioning Mew about her love for the chimps.

"What would happen, Mew, if you were not there? Would they all cry and be sad?"

"Go to sleep, June. Stop asking daft questions. Where else would I be? We will always be here for the animals."

June did not sleep. Instead she lay listening to the wind beating against the windows at the front of The Oakfield, wondering how big the zoo might grow and how soon she would be sharing her bedroom with all kinds of animals. She decided that they all needed love and communication but with their own kind. Physical contact was essential to them. She wondered if Punch needed a wife. Was he lonely in his pen?

Her mind began to wander as she lay awake. Suddenly she was startled by a door slamming, a thick oak door near to her bedroom. She sat up in bed to listen. She heard voices, quiet at first and then very loud. Two people were arguing with each other.

It was her mother and father. Voices drifted towards her; she heard odd words and knew this was serious. She also felt very guilty as she should not have been listening.

"This is my bedroom and you are not welcome in it." That was her mother's voice, slightly trembling but firm.

"They mean nothing Lizzie, nothing. Let me come in."

There was silence. Then very quietly but distinctly she heard her mother again.

"I told you about it at Shavington and you never listened. It's too late now. This is how it will remain."

A door closed. Footsteps led away down the stairs and the house slept again.

June sat up in bed, puzzled. She dared not wake Mew. She would have to work it out for herself. Soon she was snuggled up with her feet on the hot-water bottle, dreaming of Charlie climbing the oak tree to find the secret bird treasure. Instead he found a huge bird's nest crammed full of June's school books.

The following morning the incident had somehow managed to merge with June's dream world and she hardly gave it another thought. Her mother was in the kitchen, preparing breakfast. Her father was out on the lawn talking with Grandad. All seemed well in June's zoo.

1938 was a year of public confidence in Chester Zoo. The Duke of Westminster opened his gardens at Eaton near to Chester to the general public on a Sunday in June. Admission was a shilling with all proceeds going to the North of England Zoological Society, namely Chester Zoo. Free advertising was offered in seven newspapers.

The zoo had started with thirteen members and now had 220, plus thirty associates and nearly twenty-five acres of land on which to develop. But it still required £500 from founders and £250 from benefactors in order to help turn Chester Zoo into 'the Whipsnade of the North'.

Mr Mott went down to Portland to pick up more animals that had been sent over on one of the Holts' ships from West Africa. He collected a carload of animals, carrying them back in his little Hillman.

On one of these occasions he travelled to Hamburg aboard the ship, for it sailed there before docking at Liverpool. In Germany he visited Hardenbeck's Hamburg Zoo. Hardenbeck was an interesting man, well ahead of his time in planning zoos. However, he was something of a showman, and showmen and academics did not and do not mix readily in the animal world.

June loved to meet her father when he brought back the animals in his small car. On one occasion he drove down to Portland to collect animals, offered as a gift by the Governor of Nigeria, Sir Bernard Bourdillon. When the car stopped for petrol people were amazed by the travelling zoo. He carried four crowned cranes, twenty weaver birds, two cave rats and Judy, a nine-month-old lioness required to spend six months in quarantine, along with Bones, a young tiger, yet another new acquisition,.

Mr Mott laughingly explained the journey that night to his family. Judy was a glossy, plump cub, full of fun and tricks. The car was crammed with wildlife with the two men occupying the two front seats. At Portland no one thought Mr Mott would fit the lioness into the car but he explained that on one occasion he managed to squeeze twenty-seven monkeys, a chimpanzee, a porcupine, a civet cat and thirty small birds into the Hillman, so he could surely manage this lot!.... And he did!

The two rats were placed in airy biscuit tins on the floor, in front of them were the weaver birds, and on top sat Judy in her crate from where she had an excellent view through the window. The only remaining problem was the four crowned cranes but Mr Mott had an answer for that. They were each placed in a sack with a hole cut in the top so that their heads protruded. Then a piece of cord was tied under their tails. They were quite comfortable and they and the weaver birds sang all the way to Chester, occasionally interrupted by throaty growls from Judy.

A Russian bear named Trotsky arrived at the zoo, given away by a pet owner who couldn't manage him as the cuddly little animal grew fast and proved to be a little more boisterous than a teddy bear. Won Lung a Himalayan bear joined him and the two cubs were much admired by the visitors. Won Lung became Lizzie's favourite animal and she kept a special eye on both cubs, which lived in pens in the courtyard. More and more unwanted exotic pets arrived. There were extra mouths to feed and the zoo was still in debt.

An appeal for donations, signed by Lord Leverhulme, the Bishop of Chester, the Mayor of Chester, Mrs Phyllis Brown and others, was put out in the Daily Mail. It added that over the previous four years the financial losses were decreasing; 110,000 visitors had visited the gardens during those years; and it was obvious that a public need was being admirably serviced. For the zoo to continue to expand in order to accommodate the ever growing number of animals, funding must be increased. The zoo was not a profit-making organisation and no one could hold shares in it.

Around the kitchen table in The Oakfield, Lizzie and Mr Mott scrutinised the costs for the feeding programme, worried and concerned about the extra funding which was required to keep things running smoothly. It was a very worrying time for the zoo.

Malay sunbear with June (no 11 on the zoo map)
- First open enclosure at Chester Zoo

"OUR ZOO NEWS"

A monthly chronicle of news of The North of England Zoological Society.

Number One.   November 1937.

Each month a short summary of events at the Zoo will be issued to all members, and this will be headed "Our Zoo News." By this means we hope to keep members, especially those that live a long way off, informed of what is happening at the Zoo.

It is very appropiate that our first Zoo News should contain the announcement of a birth of some importance to the Zoological World.

The pair of Mandrills which were presented to the Society by R. Hyde Esq., in December 1935 gave birth to a daughter on the 25th October. As far as is known this is the first occasion that the Mandrill has bred in this country.

Some idea of the proposed Lion Accommodation may be gathered from the following.

It will be divided into two sections, indoor and outdoor. The Lion House or indoor portion will contain four cages, the larger ones which are now completed are those in which the public can see the animals. This section was opened on the 19th October by The Right Honourable The Viscount Leverhulme, and has been enthusiastically received by the public.

The smaller cages which will be at the rear of these will be used for the dual purpose of holding the Lions during cleaning operations, and providing quiet accommodation for breeding Lions.

The outside Enclosure will be surrounded by a stone and concrete wall sufficiently high to prevent any possible chance of escape, and will follow the boundary line of the Zoo from the new Lion House for about 200 feet. It will then strike straight across towards the old kiosk and sweep round towards the present Penguin Pool. It is at this point that Lord Leverhulme laid the Foundation Stone of the open-air Enclosure.

The public will be able to walk along the top of the wall from where it leaves the boundary, and at the east end of this wall terraces will be built under which it is proposed to build cafes etc.

To prevent any possible risk of anyone falling into the Enclosure a special arrangement of a wall will be erected which will not permit anyone to stand on, or lean over. As many trees as possible will be left in the Enclosure, and rocky mounds will be built to enable the public to view the animals from all angles.

The whole of the work is being carried out by the Zoo staff, and the cost of materials is being met by donations. Providing sufficient money is subscribed it is hoped to complete the whole of the outdoor accommodation by the late Spring.

13

'1939 brought war to Britain'

September 1939 brought war to Britain. For months the warnings in newspapers, conversation in the local village and young men appearing in uniform signalled unrest and anxiety. Older men who well remembered the Great War were reawakening to the deeply ingrained terrors of that bloodbath in Europe and prayed that Britain would not be involved. George Mottershead was one of them.

It was inevitable, the steady march towards the horrors of war. June heard the words 'necessary', 'invasion', troops, 'Hitler', and 'Jews'. It meant very little to her but the word 'Jews' made her question her mother about an incident that had occurred late the previous year.

Bringing a doctor in to the zoo for a member of the family was very expensive, to be avoided if at all possible, but on one occasion her mother called one in to attend to Mew who was suffering from an infected cut on her arm. The doctor was Jewish and a sensitive man who was a good friend to Mrs Mottershead. June witnessed their goodbye on the steps of The Oakfield.

"I am so sorry, but you know how it is. There will be so few patients for you now."

"I understand, I understand. It is an irrational hatred. There is more to come, much more. I must leave to live in America, for safety reasons, you know." So saying, he shook hands with Lizzie who looked dejected and sad.

Later June asked her mother why the doctor had left Chester but Lizzie refused to talk about it. She told her young daughter not to worry her head about such matters; they had the zoo to look after. That was their priority. But June did worry, beginning to watch grownups very closely, wondering how the approaching war would change her life in the zoo.

Mr Mott announced that at some future date Chester Zoo might officially close for the duration of the war. Food would become scarce for humans, let alone animals, but the Mottersheads were quietly determined to keep the zoo open. They must and would manage. It was decided that the aquarium in the cellar beneath The Oakfield would be used as an air raid shelter, and all people dressed in the uniform of H.M. Forces would only pay a half price entrance fee. The zoo would receive a warning by telephone if there was an air raid about to take place. This would give the Mottershead family time to lock up all the animals.

Already the blackout had started. Every window and lighted space had to be covered when night fell as enemy planes were searching for the port of Liverpool and Upton was on the flight path to that city. Bombs would inevitably go astray and all cities would be a target. The Oakfield would also have to observe the blackout.

Fortunately, the zoo was some distance from Chester, but two miles was of no consequence to a bomber pilot. No one at the zoo wanted to be an air raid warden, walking around during an air raid, so June was co-opted to be one. Delighted to be thought useful, she proudly took possession of a tin hat and was sent on a course on how to deal with incendiary bombs. She took great delight in crawling through a smoke filled room, and being taught how to use a stirrup pump.

June was thirteen years old.

Staff numbers dwindled as men and women were called away to help the war effort. June pricked up her ears. So here was something for her to be involved in at last. Her jobs around the zoo would be increased, particularly when the keepers were called away to war.

In April 1939 Chester Zoo had liabilities of £6,713-5s-2d. During that same month The Zoo News was printed and renamed Our Zoo News and Guide. June's job helping with the original duplication by hand in the office had finished.

June was given the tiresome, task of bringing the parrots into The Oakfield on cold nights. One particular parrot hated females so the capture of this bird had to be carried out under cover of darkness. June dreaded the great, vicious beak but she persisted with its capture. Rob-Rob, the blue and red macaw, was a different matter. Friendly but enormously heavy, he landed on the carrying stick, moving up and down, muttering continually. June struggled to lift him, never once relinquishing her hold until she reached the house; otherwise the entire process had to be repeated.

Once inside, in the comfort of the warm kitchen the parrots moved along the tops of chairs and onto family heads, busy preening themselves and running their enormous beaks along single strands of hair. Rob-Rob, who was very much at home here, always sought out June, dividing her hair as usual into single strands and nibbling along its full length. He was always left in the kitchen overnight when the other parrots were taken to the bedroom. In the morning the chairs showed evidence of his nightly activities. He thought that they were trees, and so he took large chunks from the chair backs. No one complained.

June often brought Mary into the house during the winter cold. She was very strong and, fully grown, had broken the strong steel netting of her pen, twisting the wire with her fingers, and she had also taught Kiki and Tarzana how to throw any thing available. The other chimps quickly followed, much to the amusement of the visitors, but they persisted with this trick whenever they wanted something. Mary seemed to believe that she could walk around freely with the Mottershead family.

There was great interest in the griffon vultures as they were once more building their nest. Every January and early days of February this had been carried out since their arrival in 1932. Each year they had laid one egg, which was removed once it appeared because it was invariably addled. When at last, in 1936, an egg actually hatched the vultures ate the baby!! Mr Mott's greatest wish was for a successful rearing of a griffon chick. The second successful hatching ended in the death of the chick, which was drenched in a thunderstorm, as it was not fully feathered. Mr Mott continued to wait patiently for, as far as he knew, there had never before been a successful hatching in captivity.

Despite the worry of the war, plans went ahead for the extension of the tropical aquarium beneath the mansion. These plans and proposed additions to Chester Zoo were presented at the Merseyside branch of the British Empire Naturalists' Association when they were invited as guests to the zoo. Once again it was a case of the zoo being a showcase, a working and successful zoo despite the problems of finance and threat of imminent closure.

"Lizzie, make sure we can conjure up a really splendid tea, one of your specials. The ham and salad always does the trick, followed by tea and scones."

"I'll do my best, George, we all will – but money is getting very low."

Lizzie smiled, a slow smile of understanding and loyalty. She loved her husband and fully shared in his dreams of a zoo without bars and together they would rise to the challenge. She certainly wouldn't let a World War get in her way!

Two weeks later the report from the Naturalists' Association was published in several national newspapers:

"Plans for Chester Zoo include an extension of about ten acres and the converting of a woodland ravine into a new bear pit.

The kites will be housed in the old monkey houses, and new houses will be completed by Easter.

Mr Mottershead, Secretary of Chester Zoo, informs us of Black-necked ibis' expected to arrive in a week.

The Zoo is one of only three non-profit making, purely scientific societies of its kind in the country.

Bound by its regulations to spend all its money on the animals in the zoo, it is not a business concern.

There were over a thousand visitors last month.

Chester Zoo now has its own monthly magazine, run by its members, and its influence has even been mentioned to scientists in Nigeria.

The Malayan bears living in a large open-air enclosure were the first animals the invited guests of the association came across.

Next came two goats that had been offered for lion food. They now live permanently in a paddock with the Marabou storks.

From the next paddock the rhea, a flightless relative of the ostrich, made a booming sound like a distant ship. Two young wallabies from Dudley Zoo shared the same paddock.

We were entertained by a big Himalayan bear that spent his time dancing and rolling in his compartment and showing off his boxing style.

We passed a fine flock of ancient piebald Spanish sheep, believed to date from Biblical times.

In the monkey house a young chimpanzee continually performed somersaults and cartwheels.

A large black bear was moulting her winter coat and a griffon vulture was sitting on a single egg. We were told that one of the many cats which roam the zoo, living on rats and mice, enters their aviary and removes meat from their beaks without protest from the birds. One of our members explained this strange occurrence. The griffon vulture is a carrion-eater, devouring only dead meat and not hunting for its food.

We were shown a rare black checko, which is a variety of chimpanzee. It is extremely strong and the only one of its type in captivity in this country. There is one more in the Berlin Zoo.

We were shown the polar bear pit but assured that plans for a larger enclosure will be underway once funds are replenished.

The capybaras, giant relatives of the guinea pig, are both in excellent condition.

Our members were very impressed by the many birds in the aviaries as they exhibited their brilliant colours. They were surrounded by colourful flowers, making the area very attractive.

The Liverpool Zoo has now closed. Here at Chester Zoo we are fortunate that there has been no crowning of rose queens, lemonade queens, railway queens or beauty contests. There are no dog shows, dirt tracks or displays of fireworks.

What we have here is a fine collection of animals in clean, healthy conditions and not living in prison as in the small travelling menageries, but in a life of leisure and luxury like the Ritz Hotel."

June's father laughed aloud at the final comment in the newspaper. He was pleased. "Here, June. Cut this out and add it to your scrapbook. One day it will be good to look back on."

June stuck it into a large black and red leather-bound book given to her for that purpose, although she doubted that anyone in her family would have time to look back on newspaper articles. They were all too busy living and surviving in the zoo.

May 1939 was a time of celebration for another family. Mr Mott telephoned the press to announce the hatching of the griffon vulture egg. The parents were feeding their chick, which looked in good condition. There had been no record of a chick being reared in Britain before.

Many photographers visited the zoo but were under strict supervision to take photographs only from a distance. However, the birds were settled and each day the chick grew larger, quickly becoming thickly feathered. June was excited. Even Mew, who was usually not particularly interested, glanced into the aviary from time to time. It was very good publicity for the zoo at a time of hardship and the real possibility of it closing because of the approaching war.

Staff began to disappear as the effects of the conflict bit deeply into the rural areas of Britain. A number of girls came to the zoo, working alongside a keeper. It was hoped that they would provide a substitute for the men who would shortly be called to military service.

One night Mew, June and their mother were sitting in the kitchen discussing the day's events. Suddenly they heard voices and quick footsteps. A lady keeper burst into the kitchen, bringing with her a younger woman who had commenced work in the last two weeks.

"Mrs Mott, can you help? Look at the state of her!"

Everyone turned to look at a bedraggled and shocked young woman whom June recognised from an incident two days before. Charlie had been laughing as he had seen her applying make up and complaining that the wind had blown her hair into knots. He didn't think she'd last long in the zoo. But it wasn't the wind this time; it was thick oily vomit that stank out the room. Mew bit the side of her cheek to stop herself laughing outright, and June began to giggle until silenced by her mother's stare.

"Sit down, dear. You're clearly in shock. What has happened?" But the young woman simply trembled, desperately trying to wipe the frothy sick from her face and clothes.

"Well, Mrs Mott, she was doing a night round with me when she took the wrong door, you see, and . . ." The keeper's voice trailed away as she also began to see the funny side of things.

Mrs Mott frowned. "Be sensible all of you. This girl is in shock. It's no laughing matter. Now continue May, please."

May rolled her eyes and tried to avoid looking at the girl who had now started to cry, sure of having gained the Mrs Mott's sympathy. "Well, she landed up with the vulture, you see."

'Good job she didn't land up with the lions', June thought to herself.

"Well, you know the way they disapprove of anyone disturbing them, particularly at roosting time. They vomited the remains of their last meal and..."

Mew joined in now. "Oh yes, liver and horse head if I remember correctly."

The girl now howled and rubbed the vomit from her ears in desperation.

"Well, she panicked, Mrs Mott. She was so shocked she just stood there. I've never seen so much s . . ."

"That will do, May. Say no more! Take the girl to the bathroom and explain that she must wash thoroughly. Even then the terrible smell will still be there for some days. The oil has soaked into her skin. Mew; lend her some of your clothes. Now off you go, the three of you, and you, June, can get off to bed. You have a big day tomorrow."

When the kitchen was finally empty, Mrs Mott allowed herself a little chuckle. Living in a zoo was no easy matter. It was a daily challenge and she knew with certainty that they had just lost another member of staff!

June was soon laughing, telling the story to Charlie. It confirmed all his previous thoughts about the girl. "Good job she's gone. It very well might have been in with the lions next. Fancy frightening the vultures like that!" and he burst out laughing as June stuck her fingers down her throat, pretending to be sick.

A shout from the direction of the lion pen brought the pair running over to see why three keepers had gathered outside the gate. The adult lions were kept behind bars throughout the war. Standing next to the bars was a very distressed man. His wallet was inside with the lions! He had removed his coat and was carrying it over his arm for a while. Stopping to rest, he had left it on a bench and two boys had sneaked his wallet from the pocket and pushed it through the bars.

"My return ticket is in that wallet, " he wailed. "I am from London and I must get it back even if the wallet is ruined."

So began a tricky protracted quest to recover the ticket whilst June and Charlie watched, bemused by the turn of events. Every effort was made by the keepers to distract the lioness, which was pawing at the now opened wallet. Finally she retreated. Unfortunately, she quickly returned with the other lions, one of which pawed the wallet in curiosity.

At last the keepers recovered it but as they dragged the wallet towards the gate the ticket fell out. "Quick, get the brush. We can sweep it out," but just as they were about to do this the lioness re-emerged, sniffed at the ticket, licked it and swallowed it! June and Charlie laughed about the incident as they made their way back to the house.

Charlie told June about the comments from the housing estate that was now built next to the zoo. "Some visitors had arrived and they heard the sound of ships. They said they didn't realise the houses were so near to the sea. Of course, it wasn't the sound of ships but the rhea calling. He had a voice like the ships on the Mersey!"

Exchanges of animals had started between zoos amongst them two lion cubs which came to Chester from Belle Vue. Lizzie kept a daily eye on the cubs and they settled in well. Unfortunately, in their second year they contracted feline distemper and died, much to the regret of everyone.

Bristol Zoo followed with interest the growth of the small zoo and contributed three lionesses. In 1939 a healthy lion named Patrick came from Dublin Zoo. Although Patrick was very seasick during the crossing from Ireland, he soon recovered and so began a breeding programme that would produce lions that would eventually be sent to all parts of the world. Within months he had settled well into his new life. After a mating on the eighth of August the first of many cubs was born. June was intent on communicating with Patrick, visiting him often with a miniature terrier named Jet that had grown up with the zoo animals. The lions had an indoor pen in the courtyard and June was able to visit them quite easily.

She had lain in bed listening to their roaring, thinking about their homeland and wondering what they made of their new surroundings. Knowing very little about lions, and with only the formal education of geography and the brief information in her animal atlas, she had already been witness to the death of the two cubs. Now there were three lionesses and a huge male. They would require a large amount of horsemeat and very careful handling. Her father had talked about establishing a pride, the planned breeding programme and the essential new housing for them.

The much-needed visitors, on approaching the lion pen, sometimes found themselves sprayed copiously by Patrick marking out his territory. The smell of his urine was potent and unpleasant, and Mew and June would grin at one another. However, it was not helpful to the zoo to upset the visitors. Besides, they knew their father was already searching for more finance for spacious re-housing projects.

Patrick was a magnificent animal, sprawling lazily and then standing occasionally to shake his great mane. In the evenings, when all the day's visitors had left, he never approached the bars to listen to June because he was fully preoccupied with his growing family.

Soon June heard her father calling for her dog Jet to go on one of their regular ratting expeditions. Like all terriers, Jet was an accomplished ratter and, too late, June saw one of the rodents slinking along the side of the wall. Jet gave an excited bark and the chase was on.

The rat scuttled under the bars and entered Patrick's pen. Jet followed and immediately the lion was upon her, grabbing her in his mouth before releasing her. Desperately the little terrier managed to crawl back out of the pen but she was very badly mauled.

June let out a cry of anguish. The little black bundle lay against the door as Patrick charged the bars. Mr Mott picked the little dog up and carried it to The Oakfield.

June raised her voice and all the anger that had been building inside came pouring from her: "I hate all this! I hate fund raising and being nice to people who laugh at animals, and what's more . . . " she turned, glaring at her father, "I hate the zoo - and if anyone should have a new pen it should be Punch!"

With those words she ran off to hide herself in the shrubbery, even though she heard her name being called time after time. Here she sat and sobbed, relieving all the pent up emotion and complexities of a girl of fourteen. Later, though, when she returned to the house, she found Jet lying on a blanket inside a cardboard box and could see her horrific wounds. Only then did she accept that Jet was dead.

The zoo brought laughter and strange little incidents into the lives of local people, which helped to keep them cheerful during grim times. More and more visitors arrived to see the animals even as young men suffered for the war effort. In a strange way it seemed to offer some relief for women and their children during the war years. Chester Zoo was binding itself ever more strongly into the history, legends and very fabric of Chester and beyond.

Whitsuntide brought five thousand visitors to the zoo, all determined to enjoy themselves, if only for a few hours. The roads leading to it were thronged with hiking parties, visitors on bicycles, in motor cars, carrying babies and with children holding onto their mother's skirts, parents wheeling prams, and many people carrying picnic baskets, bags and bottles for a picnic under the shady trees. The zoo meant a break for the town people, and toddlers saw for the first time animals that had only lived for them in the pages of their picture books.

Sadly, Mary was not her usual cheerful self. She was crouched in her enclosure with her head in her arms. Mr Mott explained to visitors that she was suffering from melancholia. Visitors moved on to the other animals, leaving her to sit quietly on her own and that evening Mew brought her into The Oakfield in the hope of comforting her.

The response to the Chester Zoo War Scheme had been excellent. Donations flooded in but at the same time so did more and more animals. Some of the animals at London Zoo had been shot, as it was too difficult to feed and look after them.

"This will not happen here," Lizzie announced. "We must think of a way to feed them during this hateful war."

1939 was a memorable year in a positive manner as the War Adoption Scheme, an original idea created by Mr Mott came into existence. The animals cost £60 a week to feed; this included food for two hundred mammals as well as the hundreds of birds, reptiles and fish housed at the zoo. He introduced an 'adoption' scheme. Animal lovers across the country were asked to undertake weekly payments for the animals over a number of weeks. They could adopt any animal they liked. Smaller ones could be had for as little as 1/6d a week and bigger ones, such as bears and lions, were 14/6d a week.

Already a lady from the Lake District, Miss Tomkins-Grafton of Ambleside, had adopted Punch the polar bear for four weeks. She had been visiting Punch for some time and grown very fond of him, feeling sorry for his poor conditions. She felt that he needed a pool and was considering funding this project. In the meantime she made sure that he was fed properly.

Punch was always fierce but as he grew older he was potentially more dangerous than he had ever been. His constant pacing about inside the small enclosure was sufficient to warn all keepers to be very careful when cleaning him out. Mr Mott finally made a decision to do this job whilst a keeper stood at the outside gate ready to open it the instant that Mr Mott had finished.

Punch appeared quite unconcerned, his back to Mr Mott who quietly hosed and cleaned the pen. This appeared to work well, but one day the keeper forgot his instructions, closing the gate, which left Mr Mott fastened inside with Punch.

It was a nightmarish situation as the wall around the enclosure was fourteen feet high with scarcely a foothold, and Mr Mott was fifty years old!
Now Punch took his chance, turning swiftly to stare for seconds at his benefactor before lunging at him. Mr Mott made an unbelievable leap, hanging onto the top of the wall as his feet sought to find a small foothold but Punch had already seized his shoe, shaking it in one mighty movement.

Suddenly the sole of the shoe came off in Punch's mouth, and he fell back into the pen growling in disappointment before his next lunge. Mr Mott desperately hauled himself out of reach within those few seconds and fell onto the ground above the enclosure, wet with sweat.

That night over supper as the tale was told June fell silent, remembering the time when the horsemeat had first been fed to Punch. She was reminded yet again that however long in captivity, animal instincts were always quick to come to the fore. Thank goodness this survival instinct was also present in her father who had no need to reprimand the keeper. The nearly fatal incident spoke for itself.

Mr Mott's original idea of adopting the animals became very popular and soon became financially successful. The greatest competition was for the cane rat. First on the list was a Mr Partingon of Upton who secured him for the first seven weeks.

Many new animal evacuees had arrived since the outbreak of war so the scheme was a tremendous help. Judy a polar bear arrived in this way from Brighton and joined Punch in his pen. In November 1939 a thousand two legged evacuees had visited the zoo, all interested to see the names of the adopters fastened to individual pens and enclosures.

London Zoo followed suit, introducing a successful adoption scheme of their own. Times allowed for adoption were soon extended, and any animal that was adopted remained at the zoo, several of them for the duration of the war years. The aquarium was very expensive to take on, costing £1 a week.

June pleaded with her father to change his mind over one exception - a lioness with three cubs for 16/- a week. June and her friend, Kathleen Childs who worked in the pay box, had adopted the lion cubs aged six weeks. Mr Mott agreed, but only for one month. He knew that the cubs were growing very quickly and would need on-going financial support; otherwise they would have to be sold.

City zoos were now affected by bombing raids, closing their gates and evacuating animals to the rural zoo at Chester. No animal was ever turned away. During this time, two female leopards and a male arrived from Paignton Zoo, all valuable acquisitions. One female had an injured foot so was separated from the others for four days. Immediately she entered the pen, the adult male leapt at her, seizing her by the throat. The keepers turned hoses onto them and threw three smoke bombs into the enclosure but it was a struggle to the death. Fifteen minutes later the female fell down limp. The male had broken her neck at the base of the skull.

Charlie the penguin was still waiting for a wife although he had been adopted by Form 1J of Chester City High School. Nantwich Grammar School adopted the sleek genet.

Mr Grousell became Chairman of the Society on December the tenth 1939 and he held that position until January 1963. His work for the zoo over this lengthy span was phenomenal.

Mr Mott continued to make the zoo an attraction during wartime, despite the earlier prospect of the war conditions forcing its closure. He used every available piece of scrap material to keep things running, without drawing on anything needed for the national emergency, for Chester Zoo shared the national commitment to 'make do' for the war effort.

Political cartoon based on Mr Mottershead's original idea
for adoption of zoo animals
The Evening Chronicle, October 11th 1939

The aquarium situated in the cellar under The Oakfield
Number 13 on the zoo map

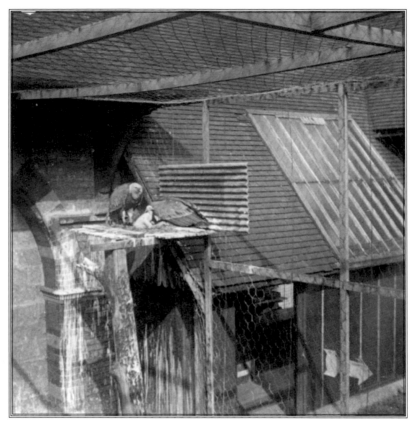

Griffin Vultures with their chick
Number 7 on the zoo map

14

'1940 was a sad time for the Zoo'

Evidence of the Second World War became apparent even to a fourteen-year-old girl living far away from city life. June was sent on a visit to the farm of her mother's parents in the Lake District, a place she had visited on several occasions. Here she enjoyed a holiday and it was a welcome break from the zoo.

On her return journey to Chester, she became aware of people in the railway carriage pointing to the bridges along the railway track. They had brief glimpses of men at each end of the bridge, holding pitchforks. A call to protect the homeland had been announced over the wireless and each small country community in England responded in its own way. Although it was slightly amusing to see such activity, June could see from the faces of the people in the carriage that this was serious. She suddenly longed to return to the zoo and her family.

Once back in school she joined the Girls' Training Corp along with a number of girls from the seniors, learning first aid and Morse. Younger girls watched in silent amazement as the Training Corp marched in disciplined lines across the school playground.

Several of the pupils scanned the innocent looking skies for signs of aeroplanes, hardly able to comprehend that their country was at war with Germany. Everyday life appeared to be so normal except for small signs such as food growing scarcer, instructions that bicycle lights must be dimmed and the subdued chattering in the schoolyard.

June and her friends swapped stories about the air raid wardens who continually patrolled at night reminding people of chinks of light showing from houses. June explained to her friends that The Oakfield originally came with roller blinds and they were still there. They were made of waxed dark blue material that did not allow any light in and paint was applied down each side of the window so no light would shine out. In any case no air raid wardens ever came into the zoo to check out the blackout, as they were always busy in the city. In the evenings she also helped her mother to cover the side windows with newspapers and criss-crossed them with strips of paper in readiness for the shattering of glass if a bomb was dropped nearby.

June spent time in the evenings writing to her mother's brother, Robert. He was in Palestine as a New Zealand soldier and enjoyed his niece's cheerful letters keeping him in touch with the family and, in particular, with his sister Lizzie.

One evening Mr Mott came in with very bad news. Peter, who had worked in the aquarium with June, had been killed, serving in North Africa. It had not been long since he'd left the Zoo and gone off to fight.

The sad news of his death reawakened memories of another conflict and for the first time June heard her father, mother, and grandparents speak of the First World War. Lizzie spoke about her two eldest brothers, both killed within months of each other. Grandfather, who had been married twice, spoke about his two eldest sons, Mr Mott's half brothers, both of whom had lost their lives in battle. His full brother Stanley was killed in the same conflagration when he was just seventeen.

Mr Mott, who had himself been badly wounded in that awful war, sat silent, listening and nodding. Suddenly he spoke, causing Mew and June to look up and listen carefully to what he had to say.

"Too many young men lie under the soil. War is a terrible, terrible thing. I deliberately refuse to talk about my own experiences during that time. Now it is happening for the second time. All over this country men and women who suffered during the First World War will relive their terrible memories and wonder at the senselessness of all of it. Soon all of our staff here at Chester Zoo will be out there fighting. Let us hope that we will see them again."

June nodded. For once she had no words.

Mew stood up, going over to stand near her mother. "I might as well tell you now whilst we are all here, discussing this awful war. I received my official papers today. I have joined the WRENS and will be leaving shortly. I am waiting to hear where I will be sent to."

A tear slid down June's cheek. Her whole world was changing and she hated it. She was angry with this war thing which had shaken her life up like a kaleidoscope, changing its pattern for ever. She was sick of her father listening to the daily bulletins, glued to the radio, sick of the struggle to feed the animals and sick of a war where precious lives were squandered deliberately. When the animals died she grieved but she could comprehend it. This was madness. She ran to her mother's side for comfort.

"Listen to me. We will be all right, all of us. Here in our zoo, surrounded by animals which need us, surrounded by visitors and supporters whose lives are brightened by visits here, we have a meaning to our lives. We shall just carry on, business as usual."

"Lizzie, good words! You are right! That's just what it will be, business as usual and that means bedtime for all of us. We need to be up early in the morning. Remember, two bison are arriving tomorrow from Dudley Zoo."

The Oakfield lay in darkness that night. There was no moon. Every member of the Mottershead family tried to come to terms with a war which raged across the English Channel, endeavouring to make some kind of sense of it. June tried to imagine her life in the zoo without her sister, and then she remembered her father's words.

Tomorrow the two bison would arrive and life would go on in the zoo. As predicted, the bison arrived early the next day. The bull was almost six feet tall, weighing just under a ton. The cow was smaller. They were released far away from the main body of the zoo, onto an undeveloped field that had been bought by a council member until the zoo could afford it.

Ferdinand was a magnificent animal, showing off his running skills almost immediately as he careered across the grass at the speed of a horse. These animals had once numbered millions, living on the rich prairies of North America, providing skins and meat to the Indian tribes. Indians, white men and wolves killed them and their numbers steadily dropped. In the winter they travelled south, migrating over a thousand miles, and reversed this journey in the summer months. Buffalo paths stamped into the prairies by the bison had been used since primitive times.

Ferdinand and his mate had this migratory instinct bred into them. Ferdinand began to wander into the adjoining fields owned by Mr Cheers. Soon a calf was born but sadly the female died when young Billy was only one year old. Ferdinand once again began to roam. In the daytime he looked innocent enough but during the nights the bison jumped the chestnut fencing which kept them in the field. Visitors complained sometimes that they could not be seen, but of course they were off visiting the neighbouring cows!

Within a few months Mr Cheers, the farmer, was complaining to Mr Mott that his cows were producing very strange looking calves, blaming Ferdinand. Mr Mott argued that the calves were not really showing physical signs of bison genes but the controversy rumbled on.

Despite Mr Mott sticking up for Ferdinand, the huge bison hated him, charging him at every opportunity. Mr Mott had once fired a shot over the bison's back to clear him off the front lawn of The Oakfield and Ferdinand had a very long grudge bearing memory.

He had no such objections towards June or her mother so it was their early morning task to return him to his field each day. By now he was 'migrating' just about everywhere and June was often startled when she bumped into his huge body in the darkness. Coming home in the blackout she could only sense the animal's presence and would try to make a detour around father and son in the dark. At weekends Ferdinand would appear on the bridle path and June would chase him back.

One day he chased some children who ran behind one of the cedars. Lizzie was called out to rescue them, but by the time she reached them Ferdinand had tired of the game and was innocently grazing on the front lawn, leaving the children peeping from behind the trunk of the tree, too terrified to move away. Mrs Mott put her foot down. The fence had to be made bison proof and with that ended both the wandering and the alleged procreation of cross-bred calves.

Cycling was a necessarily practical means of travel as petrol was rationed and there were very few cars on the roads. Coming home to the zoo on dark afternoons, June usually managed the journey with no lights on her bike but one evening she rode to Chester to meet her friends and visit the cinema. Coming home, she was stopped by a policeman who very kindly explained that she needed some dimmed lights on her bike. He rode by her side all the way back to the zoo to make quite sure she was safe.

Each morning June carried her gas mask to school but she hated it. Encased in a square brown cardboard box, and provided with string handles, it was slung over her shoulder. Once in class this contraption had to be worn for short periods at a time so that the wearer became accustomed to it. June hated the sickening rubbery smell, and the thought that she might have to wear one in an emergency was quite frightening and serious. It made the war seem much closer and more realistic.

Combined with this were the sirens that sounded when an air raid occurred. The entire school then had to rush for the air raid shelters which were dug into the Roman amphitheatre in Chester.

Every so often the family had to listen to Churchill's speeches on the radio, as Mr Mott caught up with the changing face of the war. This was followed by readings from the daily newspapers and comments on the war effort. June was becoming very bored with all of it, even though it was extremely serious.

It was a relief to go with her dad in the smelly car on Saturdays to visit the local shops where they collected promised scraps of food for the animals. Fish was no longer available and experiments began for alternative food. The sea birds were fed on strips of horsemeat soaked in cod liver oil but this did not go down too well. An alternative was oil soaked bread but several penguins and pelicans suffered and died. The lions and cats maintained a diet of horsemeat and the bears had stale bread and oats softened with milk. The aquarium was closed and used as an air raid shelter. There was no fresh fruit for the birds and the chimps suffered because of their poor diet. They caught cold and suffered chest infections which often turned to pneumonia.

1940 was a sad time for the zoo.

15

'Thanks dad! Thanks for saving them'

Throughout the 1940s the zoo was drained of male staff, resulting in a shortage of keepers even as the animal numbers increased. George Mottershead began to recruit new staff and amongst them were six girls who became keepers. They each came from entirely different backgrounds, adapting to life at the zoo quite quickly. Mr Mott felt that they were less aware of the dangers, and more relaxed than the young men he had brought in, and so the animals were more accepting of them.

One girl, Delia, was a former gown salesgirl and short hand typist. She stoked up the boilers, gave the lions their crude palm oil and 12lb meat rations and cleaned out their enclosures.

Fourteen-year-old Doreen entered the cage of the Himalayan bear, carefully handed apples to Punch, and looked after the leopards and vultures.

Twenty-three-year old Gladys, formerly a teacher, found the work at the zoo so stimulating that she was made a permanent keeper. She concentrated on the welfare of the cockatoos, parakeets and pelicans.

Their day began at 7am; they earned 7/6 a week and lived on the premises.

One spring day, Punch suddenly decided to enter his bath, sitting in the water for at least thirty minutes, until his old winter coat was floating in clumps on the muddy water. Following this procedure, he spent at least two hours vigorously shaking himself. Finally his pristine new coat was visible. June and the girls watched him in admiration.

He became suddenly aware of all the attention. Decisively he plunged back into his bath, clambered out and rolled on the concrete. Filthy again, without a backward glance he ambled into his den and refused to come out.

He continued his solitary lifestyle even though he had Judy for company but was treated with great respect as he was nearing thirty-six years of age and was the oldest animal in the zoo.

The girl keepers decided to clean out the polar bear den and renew the straw, which covered the floor. Unfortunately they forgot to close the door that connected the den to the outside pen. Punch woke up from his sleep and came out to see what was happening and of course he could then walk through the den and out of the open door to the outside world! The girls panicked but fortunately Charlie just happened to be walking past, saw what was happening and had the presence of mind to use his cigarette lighter to set light to some of the straw which lay just inside the pen. Punch was driven back and the door was quickly closed. The zoo was very fortunate to have Charlie working there for he was very quick thinking as well as being an incredibly hard worker.

Two lions, a tiger, a black panther and a leopard arrived from Bristol Zoo for the duration of the war. Food supply was at a crisis but one problem was solved by the discovery of the leopards' preference for poultry heads although they still ate their usual diet of steaks of horsemeat.

The vultures picked at horses' heads fastidiously. Stale bread mixed with oats appeared to satisfy the bears but feeding time for all the animals was growing into an enormous problem. Charlie the black-footed penguin did not enjoy eating strips of horsemeat soaked in cod liver oil; he missed the daily feed of herrings. He died after being at the zoo for seven years. Still no animals were turned away from Chester Zoo.

1941 saw the welcome arrival of two elephants to the zoo. Mr Mott told June that he had a very important job for her to carry out. The two elephants had been stranded, no longer required either by the international circus which had used them for entertainment or by their owner Ralph Marshall, who had joined the RAF. They were temporarily housed in a barn near to the town of Northampton and they and their mahout required a home for the duration of the war. They had originally come from Ceylon where their only human contact had been Khanadas Karunadasa, usually known as Kay. He was solely responsible for their welfare and their loyalty to him was total.

The alternative to sanctuary at the zoo was death. They would have to be shot. Now they were on their way by train heading towards Chester where June Mottershead would meet them. Mr Mott instructed his daughter on the route that, for publicity purposes, they must take through the City of Chester.

June was furious. How very embarrassing to be seen out on the roads of the city walking in front of two elephants. Every one would stare at her and she hated the thought of that. She wore her best dress but decided to cover it with a coat. Her cousin George would accompany her; fortunately he was staying at the zoo, although his home was in Didsbury, so at least she would have someone to talk to.

As her father drove her to Chester station, singing cheerfully as he often did, she glanced at him, wondering if he knew how angry she felt.

It was just: "Oh, by the way June, come to the railway station and walk in front of two elephants all the way back to the zoo." Or: "We must take them, June, but we have nowhere to put them!"

It was never: "June, is it all right if you could meet two elephants?"

June grew silent and moody. She wished she was old enough to be in the WRENS with Mew, well out of the way of the zoo. Everyone had to do what her father said all the time whilst he treated strangers in a far nicer way than he did her own mother. One day she meant to tell him just how she felt.

At the station a crowd of sightseers had gathered, for Mr Mott had made sure that the local community knew about the new arrivals.

The awful moment arrived and June felt a flutter of excitement despite her very bad mood. She had only once seen elephants and that had been a long time ago when she visited Belle Vue Zoo with her father to meet Mr Illes his friend. From the side of the station they came, the two great leathery pachyderms, amazing animals straight out of a storybook. A gasp rose from the crowd. On they came, solidly treading the old Roman road, Hannibal's once chosen mode of transport confidently stepping down the kerb and stopping on an order from above. June looked up to see a smiling Kay astride the first animal, sitting near to the great head and bending to whisper something in the direction of the astonishing flapping ears.

It was not after all an awful moment – it was a wonderful moment! Gone was the anger as she turned to her dad and smiled. He was so right to bring such magical creatures into the heart of a northern city of England. They could not be shot. They were incredible and fascinating.

"June will lead you," shouted her father. "I will drive back now and see you at the zoo," and he turned to go.

"Wait, Dad, wait!" June called out, running after him.

"Thanks, Dad. Thanks for saving them. We will keep them for ever, won't we, and Mum will love them."

He turned and smiled but said nothing. June suddenly realised just how tired he looked and she felt guilty about her negative thoughts. This is what mattered now, saving the animals; it was far more important than her inconsequential feelings.

Stepping in front of the first elephant she reached out and touched the leathery trunk. The sensitive moist tip explored her face and she stood quite still as Kay, the mahout, spoke some words in another language. Smiling down at her and the crowd, he introduced Molly and behind her, Manniken.

The crowd smiled, June smiled and then they were off plodding gracefully through the ancient streets of Chester.

People crowded the narrow pavements as June strode out purposely in front, making herself clearly visible to Kay. Her cousin George was at her side but there was no need for talking. They walked proudly up City Road, along Foregate Street and under Eastgate where people called out to them. June blushed but carried on. She represented her father, her mother, her grandparents and Mew, indeed, the whole zoo, and she was not about to falter now!

Turning right at the old Roman Cross she paused to glance back. The elephants stopped immediately. No sound came from them. They simply waited. Kay smiled at her with friendliness and encouragement and she continued the procession.

Turning right up Northgate Street, they proceeded with great dignity out of the City, down Liverpool Road and right at the Bache. June waved at some of her school friends who were standing on the pavement watching in admiration. Finally she led her animals down Mill Lane and up to her zoo.

It had taken two hours but for June it represented a significant milestone in her growing up.

The two elephants were housed in the courtyard next to The Oakfield in what had been the pen made for the two fully-grown chimps. Kay would take his charges for a walk around the zoo every day, stopping as they pulled branches off the trees and shrubs.

He used to bring them to the back of the house for a bath, attaching a hose pipe to the hot water tap over the sink in the back kitchen and wash them in the backyard. It took all of the hot water and no one could use the back door whilst this was being done, but who was going to argue with an elephant?

Sadly, Manniken died soon after their arrival as she was already very weak and poorly but Molly continued to be a wonderful asset to the zoo. She only obeyed Kay for she had been with him all her life. As soon as she was fully grown she gave rides to visiting children. A howdah was made to fit her, two raised platforms were built, and steps were made for the children to go up so they could be helped on to the howdah and fastened in. On the underside of one of these platforms was an old animal crate which held the seat when it was not in use. A pulley slung over the branch of a tree was used to lift it onto Molly's back.

During the winter months Molly enjoyed walks in the orchard without bearing the howdah, but as spring approached June was given the job of sitting on the howdah testing it in readiness for the summer season. Wearing it, once again irritated Molly so she would find a wall to rub against. June quickly learnt to move her legs or she would have been crushed.

Many 'adopters' visited the zoo to see their animals and a demand grew for cooked lunches. Mrs Mott and her very small staff provided a lunch of soup, fish, two vegetables, sweet and coffee for 2/3d. Lunch tickets were 2/6d including entrance to the Zoo. Meals were served between 12noon and 2pm and cups of tea and cake were available from 10am until dusk.

Grandad continued to work hard in the garden to provide food for both humans and animals.

In 1941 Chester Education Committee made an annual grant for three years so that children attending Chester schools would be let into the zoo for no cost when on school outings. Mr Mottershead was delighted as he had asked for support from the Committee.

Unfortunately, the newsletter could no longer be published as there was no one to write for it. Even June tried her hand at articles. Air raids were more frequent, resulting in the issuing of firearms to Mr Mottershead in case a bomb dropped on the zoo causing animals to escape. June could hear the shrapnel falling from the shells fired by the ack-ack battery. One piece of shrapnel actually killed a coypu, hitting it in the neck, and many pieces of shrapnel, together with the vibrations of the guns, broke most of the glass in the conservatory.

A landmine exploded at Moston causing a few windows to blow out in the courtyard. Granny and grandad were covered with soot as they sat around their fire in the Lodge. A stick of bombs fell on surrounding fields that held a herd of cows. The following morning Mr Davis the farmer collected them for milking only to find that their coats were singed by the explosions.

June lay in bed listening to the bombers flying over, the guns being fired and the shells exploding. Finally the shrapnel fell, several pieces landing on the conservatory. She heard the soldiers shouting commands for firing the gun, the ack- ack battery was that close. At first the entire family ran for safety to the cellar beneath The Oakfield but after a few weeks they simply lay in bed and listened. The following morning June would inspect the zoo grounds, collecting pieces of shrapnel.

The Mottershead family had to make sure that there was always someone to answer the telephone, day and night. Sometimes it would ring in the night alerting Mr Mott, his wife and June. They had an agreement that they would share this duty by having one night on and two nights off. These vital calls warned them of enemy aircraft overhead, which provided a red alert for the zoo, alerting staff who then checked on the animals. It was a tense time for everyone concerned.

Dr Moulden asked if his three children could be evacuated to The Oakfield for safety reasons, as people feared that Liverpool would be a prime bombing target. Mrs Mott agreed immediately and the family grew overnight. At the same time a school from Birkenhead was evacuated and came to school at the convent. June found all the sudden changes very disturbing but after a short time it was realised that the bombing was not imminent and the doctor's children returned home to the Wirral and the school children also left the area. Shortly after this, Dr Moulden enlisted and went to war, resigning as a council member.

The Oakfield was a busy place with the evacuees, the family and the live- in staff. In the evenings June used to join them when they sat around the huge black iron stove in the kitchen, laughing and joking. During the winter evenings they would play games: - consequences, spin the plate, sardines, murder, and dares such as walking right round The Oakfield in the dark. Despite the depressing daily news of the war, everyone seemed to stick closely together as one big family, determined to make the running of The Oakfield and zoo a success. There was a cheerfulness and camaraderie between all of them, which June would never forget.

More people came to live in, and Mrs Mott seemed to magic up meals for an ever-growing number of people. Never complaining, always calm and optimistic, she conjured up delicious and satisfying meals for the growing numbers. Several young people had been living in at The Oakfield since before the war. Bill was a particular friend of Charlie. They went to join up together at the beginning of the war. Bill was accepted for the Navy, but Charlie didn't pass the medical so he went to work for the Ministry of Defence, remaining in England. There was also Sam and a Welsh boy named Nippy. Eventually they also left to join the forces.

Amongst the girls were Ruby and Enid who used to help Mrs Mott with the housework and café. Enid used to polish the wooden floors in The Oakfield until they gleamed, which Mrs Mott thoroughly approved of but her husband used to rush into the house at his usual fast pace, slip and lose his footing and curse the polisher. In many ways it was an exciting time at the house with so much activity, friendly banter, conversation and jokes.

So many animals had flooded into the zoo that several of them were not securely fastened in. Ferdinand continued to wander about quite freely, much to the amusement of a British soldier who roared with laughter when he saw June chasing the massive animal off the front lawn.

Two soldiers were billeted in The Oakfield. They were barmen to the officers' station in a nearby house named 'The Lawns'. They only slept at The Oakfield, walking to their station each morning. June walked behind them as she set out for school, laughingly calling them Tweedledum and Tweedledee.

Other British soldiers, who were stationed at the Dale, used to go on a route march along Caughall Road, which passed the entrance to the zoo. The sergeant ordered them to halt by the orchard where they would 'fall out' and raid the apple trees. Mrs Mott was very upset when they did this, as the apples and pears were carefully picked and stored for food each year.

Animals were arriving all the time, but Mr Mottershead refused to send them away. Two white Bahrain donkeys from Edinburgh arrived and on the same day a black leopard also came from Edinburgh Zoo. This concerned June as she could not see him at night in the blackout if he escaped. The lion cubs were continually on the loose until they killed a sheep. Then their freedom came to a sudden end.

Strangely, it was a record season for the zoo as the visitors flocked to see all the new exhibits.

On the thirty first of January 1941, because the Council members were all doing war service, there was a proposition to close the zoo. Mr Mott and Mr Grousell, however, were determined not to let this happen, assuring the members of the Council that they could manage. The last Zoo Society meeting was held on the thirty first of January followed by the next council meeting held on April the thirtieth. The future of Chester Zoo remained very uncertain for times were surely grim.

Ferdinand the bison

Manikin and Molly with Kay

123

Kay the mahout riding on Molly with Natalie his daughter

16

'We both have mothers who collect people'

Kay moved into the bedroom that Charlie had occupied. With Charlie and most of the staff gone there was an enormous gap of expertise with the caring of the animals but Kay had great empathy with all creatures. He bathed often and used bath essence, the scent of which pervaded The Oakfield. He did this to eliminate the smell of elephant, allowing him to be closer to other animals, particularly the lions.

June had never heard of or smelt these exotic perfumes that Kay had acquired as he travelled around the countries of Europe. He also had some very well made and distinguished looking clothes, and one garment in particular caught June's eye, an expensive camelhair coat.

Kay was a great tease and laughed a lot; he was positive and cheerful. If he didn't want to do a particular task he suddenly lacked English skills, playing dumb. June wished she had this skill as she found it difficult to refuse her father when he sent her off on some strange journey or other to retrieve animals. She understood that most of the staff had left to do war work and that things were difficult at the zoo but when she was asked to travel to Liverpool docks to retrieve a monkey she was initially annoyed. Everyone was very busy and Kay urged her to go as the monkey was stranded. A pet of one of the sailors, it badly needed a home and the customs had contacted Mr Mott.

So June set off for the day, travelling through the summer sunshine aboard a bus, which took her to Birkenhead where she crossed the river Mersey by ferry. She was amazed to see the masts and funnel of a sunken ship in the river. Destroyed by a mine that the Germans had dropped in the Mersey, it was a stark reminder of the war. The overhead railway took her to the docks where the ship was berthed.

Feeling very embarrassed, she explained to the policeman at the dock gates why she needed to visit the ship, showing him the explanatory letter which

125

her father had written. The policeman gave permission for June to enter the area and directed her to the berth. It seemed a very long walk through the dockland where so many men were extremely busy, for these were the frantic darkest days of the war. Some of the workers gave her very strange looks and shouted out remarks but she held her head high and tried to ignore them. Furious with her father for sending her on such a mission she concentrated on the plight of the poor monkey and finally she reached the gangplank where a customs officer was waiting for her. She was told to wait and finally a sailor appeared, holding a cardboard box containing the monkey.

He thrust it at June as if it was a box of vegetables, turned and walked back up to the ship. Then June was faced with the same awful walk back through the docks, the coarse shouts of the men ringing in her ears, the arrival at the gate and the grilling about the box from the policeman and out at last to catch the overhead railway and the journey across the Mersey. It was only when she finally sat down on the bus that she could relax.

No one seemed to be taking any notice of her, thank goodness. She could have been carrying any household goods, not a monkey! She allowed herself a little smile, confident that the mission had been accomplished. Suddenly an old lady boarded the bus and plonked herself down next to June.

"What's in your box, love?'

Quickly deciding to act stupidly to avoid any more questions, June simply smiled sweetly and muttered something. At precisely that moment she sensed a warm wet feeling spreading across her knee. The monkey was peeing profusely and the pee began to seep through the cardboard, on to her frock and trickle down her legs. The smell was terrible.

"Oh dear, love! Something has broken in there, it's leaking out all over you! Best to open the box right now and sort it out before it gets any worse".

June was desperate. She knew she wasn't supposed to take a monkey on public transport. She stared ahead, hoping that the old woman would shut up. But she wouldn't, exclaiming loudly to the other passengers that the box was leaking. Everyone began to look at June who turned bright red with embarrassment. At the next stop the old woman got off the bus and June could settle down again and hopefully become anonymous.

June relaxed, as far as she could in the circumstances, all was well and she would soon be home. But then another pressing thought occurred to her. Her fingers began to sink into the bottom of the cardboard! Would it hold? The monkey was bouncing off the sides and June had visions of it breaking out, scampering all over the passengers. She decided to alight, getting off the bus at the next stop, which was Mostyn, about a mile from home. The road ran alongside fields. At least here, if the box disintegrated, the monkey would be in the country and there was nobody about to see it happen.

It was a nightmare of a day for June but when she finally trudged wearily into the zoo grounds no one wanted to know about her rescue mission. It was all taken for granted. No one said "How awful for you". It was simply "Job done!"

June realised that the zoo was becoming so well known that she could no longer remain invisible to the outside world no matter how shy she was. She was pleased to be able to escape to her best friend Nancy's farm where she could relax, play tennis, and go for long cycle rides with Nancy and Margaret her older sister. The three girls did most things together and June considered them to be her best friends. The friendship between the three girls was an essential part of June's growing up for it took her away from the zoo for short periods of time and was great fun. The Oakfield always seemed to be full of strangers, either evacuees, visitors or guests as her mother seemed to collect people. Nancy would laugh:

"My Mum does the same thing. We both have mothers who collect people."

One day Nancy went home from visiting the zoo puzzling over a remark made by June as she saw her friend off on her bicycle.

"I shall lock my bedroom door tonight. There is someone staying and I don't trust him."

Nothing more was added to this mysterious remark, but Nancy realised how wise June was and old beyond her years. On another occasion she had been in the kitchen with Mrs Mott when she heard the sound of sobbing coming from the hall. Going outside she saw a lady sitting on the stairs crying.

When she returned Mrs Mott smiled. Nancy decided to say nothing but Mrs Mott brought up the subject.

"Is there a woman sitting on the stairs crying?"
Nancy was shy but she knew she mustn't lie.

"Well, yes but...."

"Don't worry about it!"

Mrs Mott smiled again busying herself with preparations for the café tea. A few minutes later she left the kitchen and Nancy could hear her talking in a comforting way, explaining to the woman that Mr Mott didn't mean any of the promises he had made to her and that the relationship was over. The woman finally left.

At that moment Mr Mott came in muttering to himself.

"Has she gone?" he asked sheepishly.

"Yes," replied his wife and continued preparing salads as if nothing had happened.

Glancing at her, he headed for the side door which led to the walled garden thus escaping from whatever embarrassing situation he had put himself in.

June came in carrying a lion cub and the two girls set off for a walk around the zoo gardens which had closed for the day. June let her friend hold the animal for a while and then put him down. The cub ran off in the bushes, every so often pouncing out on the two girls, making Nancy jump with fright.

June remained totally calm. "We're his prey, Nancy, he's practising on you!"

As they walked June listened to Nancy telling about the incident in the kitchen.

"He'll do it once too often. Mum won't put up with it forever. She is the one who really keeps this zoo going, always has been."

"But June," Nancy paused, running after her friend who was striding away quickly with the lion cub now tucked under her arm. "June!"

June stopped and turned around, her expression giving none of her feelings away.

"It's not your father's fault. Women chase after him all the time. We've all seen that, you know we have. He's very handsome and lively. He scares me a bit 'cos he's so clever, but I think he loves all of you. You are his family."

June said nothing. She had her own opinion about her father's 'other women' and was not about to share it with anyone, even her best friend.

A week later June received one of the letters which she had sent to Italy to her Uncle Robert. She recognised her own handwriting. Why had it been returned? She turned the unopened letter over. In a pale hardly distinguishable text the dreaded word 'deceased' was stamped across it.

Cramming the letter into her pocket she ran upstairs to her bedroom, locked the door and threw herself onto her bed. She sobbed, for her dead uncle, for those horrible war years, for Mew, her mother and for the zoo. Finally she smoothed the sheets, dried her eyes, unlocked the door and went to find her mother.

What a terrible and cruel way to hear of your own brother's death. Putting the envelope into her mother's hands, she hurriedly left the kitchen for the gardens. She sought the place where for many years as a child she had climbed up and sat, as high as she could in one of the large trees. Down below were the dense evergreen laurel bushes which she remembered so well from her childhood. She had made a den deep inside the foliage and often hid in there. She recalled times when as a small girl she would lie and watch the changing clouds and stare up at the big tree. It didn't seem so massive now, her long limbs enabling her to climb even higher. She lay along a secure branch, dry eyed but terribly sad, watching the world below her - she had always been a watcher of people. Lying there comforted her, even when it seemed there was little in the way of consolation.

Brushing her dark hair from her face she thought about the animals. All her life it seemed she had observed and cared for them. Now she felt like one of them, out of her environment, surrounded by strangers and unable to share her feelings about this other world she loved so much; a world of patterns and shapes, loneliness in her thoughts, privacy, an unwillingness to share her observations, the feeling that she wasn't quite like the other girls at school. She seemed so much older, a bit like Punch really, still confined in the same old pens when they both desperately needed a new one.

Her father came to the front of The Oakfield and called her name. She shut her eyes tightly and did not answer. Three times he called. Finally she opened her eyes. He had gone. She lay there until it was quite dark then sadly slid down from her sanctuary.

She never climbed the tree again.

REARED IN CHESTER ZOO

17

'The greatest friendship between two animals the zoo had ever known'

Lizzie came into the house after her morning walk to check on the animals. Despite having to work all day, and no matter how many new animals arrived, she never neglected this aspect of her pastoral care.

She shook her head, stopping to talk to grandad. "I have never seen so much litter about the zoo before. The gardens are cluttered with it; it is piled up against the pens and it has even blown into our orchard."

"Yes, Lizzie. Not only that, but there has been so much petty theft and meaningless destruction since the outbreak of the war, as if things aren't difficult enough as it is."

"We have plenty of litter bins, but it is just dropped anywhere. Not only that, but there is so much thieving in the zoo this year. I can understand the children raiding the orchard but adults have been in stripping all the fruit off the trees even before it has grown. We need the apples and pears for the animals but the fruit is taken before it has ripened. Many hundredweights have been lost this year."

Grandad paused for a moment, lighting up his pipe, thinking about this dilemma.

"Maybe it's the war, you know, the way it's affected people. Most of the notices and signs have been ripped down and broken; the lavatory has been stripped of anything they can remove. Even the chain handle has been torn down."

Lizzie sighed. "The majority of visitors are fine but hidden amongst them are the vandals. If they are caught they blame someone else. But you know, it isn't just at the zoo that this is happening. Evidently last week someone objected to the film at the Gaumont. He took a knife and cut the adjoining seat."

"No pride, that's what it is, with all this fighting going on," Grandad added. "It's affected people's minds. Well, on a happier note we have never been so busy. We have had a hundred percent increase since 1939. The café increase is nearly two hundred percent over the 1939 figures. Visitors seem to appreciate our fresh food more when they have had to walk to the gardens because of travel restrictions. Well, I'd better get a move on. You wanted lettuces and cabbages, didn't you? They'll be in, in a minute."

He wandered off into the kitchen garden and Lizzie returned to her duties in the kitchen. What on earth would they have done without him over the years? Lizzie was very fond of grandad; he saw and appreciated all that she had done for the zoo, both here at Upton and back in Shavington. She wished that his wife cared for her a little more, but Lizzie had accepted a long time ago that granny considered her not good enough for her darling son George, as was often the case with mothers-in-law. In granny's opinion, Mr Mott had married beneath him. He was the apple of his mother's eye and she ignored all his misdemeanours. He could do no wrong and the situation would never change.

Lizzie brightened up as she saw June coming out of the house. How her daughter had grown! She was practically a woman now. Lizzie felt a pang of guilt. At times she felt as if she had neglected June because of the zoo. The girl had had no childhood even though outsiders thought it was a wonderful life for her. Well, it certainly wasn't. She had ridden the same undermining storms of insecurity and been badly buffeted like the rest of them, working every single day when she came from school, talking and giving her emotional all to the animals, missing Mew, even parading courageously in front of the elephants through the streets of Chester.

Lizzie was determined to make it up to June one day.

As she returned towards the house from her morning walk she realised that she had the unpleasant job of sacking those silly girls who had recently joined the zoo. Their enthusiasm had worn off and of late they had become down right dangerous. One of them had actually left a gate open on the bears last night. She'd spotted it on her walk. George always left her with the task of getting rid of inefficient people.

Her long, long day had begun; she was such a mainstay.

June had been given a puppy named Peter to replace Jet, but he divided his time between everyone in the family, unlike Jet who gave her undivided attention to June. Peter was a cross between a smooth haired terrier and a Sealyham terrier. He spent his time dashing around the zoo, interested in everyone and everything.

When Peter was about six months old, in the spring of 1942, three lions came to the zoo: Victor, his brother Valentine, and his sister Valerie. Soon the lioness left to become a regimental mascot and the two brothers settled down at Chester Zoo to become part of the future breeding stock.

Unfortunately, Valentine injured himself badly and had to be shot, leaving Victor on his own. Victor cried continually for his brother creature, nothing seeming to comfort him. Victor was still really only a cub, separated from the adult lions until he matured, so he was very much on his own, but not for long. June went into his pen to play with him, cuddling and consoling him. Her dog Peter followed her. Initially Victor was highly suspicious of the little dog, but gradually became used to him, even allowing the terrier to sit on his paws.

One day he began to lick and clean the puppy, and so began an incredible friendship. June felt confident in leaving the two of them together and Peter settled down with his new friend. After what had happened to Jet, June could only marvel at such an unlikely pair of friends.

That night June attempted to take Peter into the house, but he resisted strongly, running back to Victor. June insisted, but as soon as she walked away with Peter firmly held in her arms Victor began to howl, and the little terrier barked continually.

Throughout the night Peter refused to settle in June's bedroom whilst Victor constantly moaned. As soon as Peter was released into the grounds he ran to Victor's pen, refusing to move. By the time June returned from school the decision had been made: Peter could take up permanent residence with Victor. They shared the same bed, ate together and were inseparable.

Each day Peter was let out for exercise and sometimes he returned to his old bed, by the fire in The Oakfield. June only had to say the words; "I wonder how Victor is?" and Peter would rush off to visit his companion.

Months went by and Victor was growing into a fine male lion but still the friendship held between the two animals. The original film 'The Jungle Book' was showing across the country, stimulating yet more interest in zoos. It was released in Chester in September 1942. Mr Mottershead was very impressed by the film, which inspired him to rename Victor. He would become 'Mowgli' after the character in the film.

A ceremony was planned. Many famous people were asked to perform the renaming which meant laying a tentative hand on Victor and gracing him with his new title. No one came forward to undertake this duty but fortunately a young journalist from Southport, Joan Hyland finally offered to do the honours.

On a Saturday afternoon, with an audience that included a bishop, the managers of the cinema and the music hall, the publicity manager of the Gaumont cinema, Mr Mott and various onlookers, the renaming ceremony took place.

June knew how important it was to have Peter there and stood nearby to see the reaction of Victor towards the young woman journalist. She stepped forward and, gently touching him on his head, she pronounced him Mowgli. He snarled a little and showed his teeth, ensuring a hasty retreat from his pen, but Peter bounded forward to calm him. Mowgli then enjoyed a juicy shank bone watched by his friend, indifferent towards the clickings of many cameras.

Every so often Mowgli would lift his head to growl at his audience but instantly Peter playfully tried to drag the large bone away from him. He settled down to the serious business of eating.

June was amused by the ceremony for it was perfect publicity for Chester Zoo.

That evening Mr Mott was also laughing about the strange friendship but June was concerned when she heard of his future plans for Mowgli.

"In a few months that pair will have to be separated. The lion is almost mature and I will reintroduce him to the others as part of the breeding programme."

"I don't think it will work, Dad, it will go wrong. Peter and Mowgli, as we now have to call him, are too attached to each other. They will both pine."
Her father was adamant, and no further discussion could take place.

Shortly after this conversation, June went in search of Peter, finding him in his usual place. She smiled as she saw him hanging onto Mowgli's whiskers, jumping on his back, biting his tail and teasing him. She thought of all the visitors who had warned that Peter would become food for the lion one day. Mowgli only had to taste Peter's blood and that would be the end of the little dog.

She heard a yelp. Mowgli had accidentally placed one of his great paws down on Peter's tiny paw and burst open the pad. Blood seeped out. June kept very still and watched. Fortunately no one else was near. Mowgli took Peter gently in his mouth, lifting him onto giant paws and set about licking the blood to clean the deep cut. Such was the bond between them, the tiny spirited dog and the powerful lion, true companions across the species barrier.

June finally left school in 1943 to a very uncertain future. Fearing that the zoo might still close, her mother insisted that June must train for some other kind of employment. She decided on hairdressing and went off to Chester for six months to begin an apprenticeship. She was never far removed from the needs of the zoo, helping each evening and on Sundays as more and more visitors came, many attracted by the celebrity of Mowgli and Peter.

Lizzie was worried about granny who appeared to be even more distant, forgetting things and causing great concern for grandad. The doctor was called; the diagnosis was the early signs of Alzheimer's disease. June was needed to help full time at the zoo, so she returned, working seven days a week and being paid for the first time. This relieved some of the pressure on her mother who could spend more time looking after granny.

Lion cubs were being sold for £50 each and the zoo sold ten in ten months. Yet again Mowgli's destiny was mentioned, but he was such a crowd puller that for the time being he was left with Peter.

Mr Mott and Mr Grousell were determined not to let the zoo close despite the mounting difficulties. June was called to take the legal papers for Miss Allen to sign as their guarantor, spending the whole day on and off buses across the Cheshire countryside until she finally reached Miss Allen at the convalescent hospital which she managed. It was a relief to find her, still in her uniform; so the papers were signed and witnessed, and June made her way back to the zoo.

By April 1943 the net profit for the zoo was £467.1s.0d, which was the deciding factor in managing to keep it open. Building and maintenance materials were now impossible to find, resulting in enclosures becoming very shabby and insecure for the animals. Several of the pens were falling into disrepair. There were no essential developments of bear, lion or elephant enclosures during the war. The lions remained in their indoor pen, which was approached from inside the courtyard. Molly the elephant still had her stall in the courtyard and the bears were also housed there inside their wire pens. Much rebuilding remained to be done.

Miss Tompkins Grafton offered to pay for a new enclosure and pool for Punch and Judy but it was delayed, as government permission was needed. The threat of invasion was well and truly over, but fighting still continued in Europe as Germany was forced back on itself. Any spare building supplies which were available were sent immediately to bombed areas in the cities for rebuilding of houses and factories.

Grandad and granny celebrated their Golden Wedding anniversary in 1943 but it was tinged with sadness, as granny was evidently ill. Later that day Mr Mott announced his decision concerning Mowgli. He would have to break his friendship with Peter. They had been together since 1942 and proved to be one of the major attractions to the zoo, but there were many lionesses which were required to mate and Patrick was the only other adult lion. He was the father of the lionesses so he could not breed with them. Nero, another lion, had sired six cubs but he had died. Mowgli must take his place, and it would also relieve the problem of renewing Mowgli's cage which was hardly adequate for a full-grown lion. Peter could easily run in and out but shortly Mowgli might successfully do the same, as the wiring was old and rusty.

The following day the two friends were separated, thus ending a long friendship which would be remembered by thousands of visitors to Chester Zoo. June was apprehensive, feeling that they should stay together, but she could not interfere. Peter had restricted walks, as June did not want him to run into the other lions to look for his friend. She still had those bad memories of Jet.

The days that followed were a nightmare to June. Both Mowgli and Peter began to fret. Mowgli was transferred to the lion house and gradually introduced to the lionesses. Peter was allowed to see him before the meeting took place. Mowgli then appeared to miss Peter more than ever. He became terribly excited and agitated, pacing up and down and working himself into a sweat. Suddenly the weather became very cold and Mowgli caught a chill. It rapidly turned into pneumonia.

A paraffin stove was hurriedly erected, as there was no heat in the lion house. Under swift instructions from June's father, straw was heaped around Mowgli as he lay on his side, panting. Keeping him warm was the only remedy as it was impossible to give him anything.

Fate worked against him. A strong gale blew up, almost extinguishing the stove which gave off very little heat. Within three days Mowgli's condition worsened. Peter was brought in to be with his friend and he lay quietly by his side as the stricken animal slipped into unconsciousness. He died in the early hours of the next morning.

Mr Mott now wished that he had never separated the two friends. He made a statement to the press adding that had the enclosure with its dens and communicating passages been completed, the tragedy of Mowgli would never have happened. It would have been impossible to move Mowgli back to his old cage, as he would have had to be crated. He was a fierce and powerful animal and only allowed Peter near to him.

The greatest friendship between two animals that the zoo had ever known had finally come to the tragic end that June had foreseen.

Once Mew had left the zoo everything seemed to change. She had worked relentlessly and now she was gone. She was stationed in many places around Britain during the war but initially she was posted to Wales. June and her mother made several journeys to visit her, staying at Criccieth. It was a long journey by train, changing at Bangor but finally they booked in at the Castle Hotel at Criccieth. From there they had to take a bus to the Butlin's camp to meet up with Muriel.

The nearby Butlin's holiday resort had been converted into a naval base with all places and signposts changed to military signage. June was very impressed by the way her sister dressed and spoke. She looked extremely smart and had been made Chief Petty Officer in charge of the cooking.

"Well, the zoo did something for you then," smiled her mother as they laughed about Mew's first experience upon arriving at the camp. Her first order had been 'Right, make the salads!'

She'd certainly heard those words before!

She shared a small chalet with another girl and whilst their mother was resting, June and Mew walked for a short while around the camp which was swarming with navy ratings and a few distinguished looking officers. Many of the WRENS spoke to Mew as they passed by. June was envious. If only she could have a life like this but what would happen to her mother? Mew may have gone but she couldn't leave her mum on her own.

"Mew?"

"What now?"

Mew smiled, knowing that her sister was full of questions as always.

"Mew, have you got a boyfriend?"

June blushed but looking around she could see that her sister attracted the eye of many young men, even though her quiet dignity made her sometimes seem a little aloof.

"Well June, there has been one man I really liked but it is no use. He's not here at the camp now and anyway he's married."

"Oh!"

June was disappointed but curious she asked what he did. The reply was brief.

"He was a Dutch Captain. Now no more on that subject June, and don't tell Mum!" she warned.

Back at the hotel that night she thought about just how self contained her sister was. The hotel was swarming with Australian airmen, all in training in the area. Mew wasn't short of choice, she decided. As for her, it was back to the zoo in a few hours and more work and the same old routine. Would she ever be free of it?

Four weeks later she made the journey to Bangor on her own and met up with Mew for the day. Happy to see each other again they walked along the Menai straits in North Wales, a beautiful stretch of wooded countryside. The winter snows covered the mountains but as they walked into the woods, the contrast was startling. The grey water of the Menai, the dark woods and the dull sky stood in startling contrast with the Snowdonia mountain range.

They plodded on, June as always walking behind her sister as she had done as a child. It was like old times, except that Mew was dressed in uniform, and June was now seventeen years of age.

Then they were out on the edge of the woods, looking out over the suspension bridge and the troubled waters below.

"I imagine New Zealand to look like this."

June stopped walking as Mew turned around.

"What's made you think about New Zealand, Mew? It's a long way away."

"Well, when the war is over I want to travel. You know that June. I have often talked to you about it."

June felt troubled. Surely Mew would eventually return to the zoo?

"Yes, but I always thought it was because of our animals, I mean that you wanted to see where they actually came from."

"Well, there's something in that, but I want to travel on my own. I have always been interested in New Zealand. Remember all the letters from Uncle Robert, and he was in the New Zealand forces. Anyway, don't worry about any of it June. It's a long way off and maybe one day you will travel too."

June knew that they both wanted to be released from the zoo as it had always consumed their lives, before anything else and anyone. She was silent and Mew tried to cheer her up.

"We've got a good Dad. He has always cared for all of us."

June felt very angry. "Well that might be the case! but you know what Mew? ... I have always wondered if we have any other brothers and sisters."

She waited for the full impact of her words to affect Mew, but her sister appeared to be quite unmoved.

"Dad is very strong. He's had five people depending on him, and he's never let us down."

"I suppose you're right. Anyway the zoo has turned a corner. There are lots of visitors now."

Mew smiled. How well she knew her little sister.

"How is grandad? I know it's not easy with granny being so ill. And mum? How is she? And what is happening around the zoo?"

"They are all managing but we miss you so much Mew."

Mew decided to come straight to the point.

"Is Dad still playing around with his ladies? He's always so discreet. He keeps it all a secret but he knows that I know."

They sat down together on the edge of the wood, confiding and comforting each other, trying to rationalise their father's behaviour.

"Mew, when did you find out about Dad?"

"Years ago, in Shavington when I found Mum out in the backyard crying. I knew what was going on, but it's never been any different. You know that June."

She looked sadly at her sister. "We grew up with infidelity, both of us."

June spoke carefully and slowly, pouring out the private thoughts which had simmered in her young mind for years.

"Mew, we might have known about it, but that doesn't make it right. It is terrible for Mum. I have heard them rowing sometimes and once a woman came to the house and...."

Her voice trailed away. She felt thoroughly miserable.

Mew spoke softly. "June, you are right but there are other things besides sex in a marriage. A woman who loves a man who has other women secretly gets very hurt. It is a betrayal of their love but Mum and Dad have stayed together because they have both embraced a dream. Dad relies on her and they stuck together for our sake, and the dream of the zoo, of course. Mum thought about leaving him, often. We have talked about it even when you were little, but Mum would never leave you and me, grandad and granny. She shares her love with the animals and us. We are a family and there is no running away."

June sighed. She felt a little better for hearing this. She loved her mother so much and also her father.

"Mew, I have always tried to figure it out by looking at the animals. Some of them find a mate for life and others have lots of wives. That's like Dad."

They both burst out laughing.

"Tell you what though, little sister, I will find one mate who will never stray, and I think you will too. Come on now. We better get going. You have a train to catch to Chester."

Then she did a surprising thing. She turned and gave June a big hug.

"I'm lucky to have such a great little sister. You've turned into a real thinker June. Now let's get going," and with that she strode ahead as usual deftly retracing her steps along the woodland path.

June followed, as always.

Back at Chester Zoo the hard work continued. The pens in the courtyard which had safely contained small cuddly bear cubs now housed fully grown powerful adults which were for ever getting out. Unfortunately the building of the new polar bear and brown bear pits would not start until late 1944 when they were moved into their new pens built on one of the fields, although plans were made long before this. Mrs Hewitt a benefactor of the zoo gave money for the building programme, permission being granted by the authorities for the buildings to start immediately. Wet weather hampered the work on the new bison enclosure. Once again Ferdinand began to wander, this time to the orchard where he became a glutton for the fallen apples.

June went to work at Williams & Williams who were making jerry cans for the war. She had been conscripted along with everyone else as soon as they had turned eighteen and been sent to work in a factory. For a few months she had to do this boring, noisy and dirty job. No longer could she help at home because it wasn't considered to be essential war work. Chester Zoo now depended on older and very young people.

She hated the tedious repetitive work so applied to go into the Land Army. In 1944 she received notice to report to a nursery at Delamere. That first long walk from the station to the nursery blistered her feet terribly in her uncomfortable shoes as she clutched her luggage and sported a heavy greatcoat. There she worked in the horticultural greenhouses and orchards. Here, working with plants, she thoroughly enjoyed her freedom. Once every two or three weeks she returned home but actually, almost ashamedly, never really wanted to.

One night June entered the local pub for the very first time. She felt out of place and very guilty, even though she had a cheerful Land Girl with her. It was the first of several visits to the pub with her worldly friend and June began to taste real freedom for the first time.

She really enjoyed living at Sandymere, which was a house similar to The Oakfield. Every morning the girls left the attic where they slept, and taking a packed lunch of bread and cheese they walked through the beautiful pleasure grounds and woods to start work. Early in the morning it was a special precious place passing the lake, through the landscaped gardens and on into the woods and the nursery.

June knew far more about horticulture than the average novice so she was given the job of fertilising the tomato plants with the aid of a rabbit's tail on a stick. Before this one of her jobs was to side-shoot and tie up the tomato plants. When she cut out the side shoots to make the plants stand to attention she often wondered if she was hurting them. It was a strange thought but June thought of the plants as very much alive. Down the rows June went, dusting each tomato flower with a rabbit's tail. It was delicate work which needed consistency and grandad's training literally bore fruit.

Another of her jobs was to spread manure round the base of the fruit trees. It was heavy work and soon she had large segs on her hands. She was really happy there, home worries slipped away and she was dismayed when she was told that she had to move after six weeks, as she was only temporarily replacing another Land Girl. The head gardener wanted to keep June but the job had already been promised to someone else.

So it was moving time again and this time they insisted she went to Hoole Hall and billeted at home. Every day she cycled to Hoole Hall and back again, and the sadness of losing friendships was eased as new friends were made. She felt uncomfortable though when the American convoys passed her, weaving in close to the bicycle, whistling, shouting and waving. They were on their way to Europe for D Day and heading for Liverpool.

With the threat of invasion long over and as the allied forces prepared to push back against the Germans, limited building materials became available to Chester Zoo, allowing the government to give permission for some urgent building to take place, although it was mainly repair work.
Building commenced immediately to construct much needed lavatories in the back drive of The Oakfield. Up until this time visitors had to use the one lavatory situated in the side entrance to the house opposite the steps down to the cellars which had housed the aquarium before the war.

The top priority when building had begun was the broken dens and aviaries. The aviaries were in a terrible condition, hardly recognisable as the bright interesting places to visit before the war. June wandered round, pausing to talk to Punch and wondering when at last he would have his pool completed.

Labour was now an enormous problem at the zoo. Mr Mott had always tried to find staff that had empathy with the animals but the war had made employment very difficult. Many soldiers were being discharged, often due to injury or battle fatigue, but return to civil life was not easy for them and they found it difficult to settle down. Work at the zoo had to be consistent as success with the animals meant a strict daily routine and reliable staff.

June was now working outdoors with her father, or inside in the café which she hated. Like her sister Mew she preferred jobs which involved the animals but now she had to be able to tackle just about any task. However, she really enjoyed holding the new wire as her father endeavoured to mend broken enclosures and it was good to work together for a while.

A new roadway appropriately named Bison Drive was being prepared across the field where Ferdinand and his new wife lived. During this time Mr Mott could be spotted frequently as he inspected the new drive. As usual he never appeared to walk around the zoo, always going at a trot. June used to make her mother laugh as she described her dad as a whippet, he moved so quickly. He was asked to participate in BBC Broadcasts on the wireless with news and adventures from within the zoo. Children loved the broadcasts, looking forward to the news, hopefully followed by a visit.

In May 1945 the Second World War ended in Europe. June was unaware of this. She was busy planting out lettuce! Within hours of rumours that war was finally at an end, officialdom pronounced that the conflagration was really over and the enormous sense of relief which followed was nationally overwhelming.

Finally June was discharged from the Land Army, once more returning to the zoo, feeling bitterly disappointed as she felt that her freedom had been curtailed.

Victor the lion being renamed Mowgli (no 2 on the zoo map)

Peter and Mowgli in the lion's first pen

Mowgli as a fully grown lion

Mr Mottershead interviewing Mr Iles for the BBC at
Belle Vue Zoo

Hay making at Hoole Hall (June in centre)

June in the Land Army

18

'Take me with you, Mew'

Now that the war had ended the aquarium was to be opened up again. When June took on the position of aquarist she tentatively entered the cellar which housed the tanks. It was in a terribly neglected state but she had been told by her father to sort it out ready to reopen. June tackled all of this entirely on her own.

At the beginning of the war a temporary member of the staff had put the cold-water fish in warm water and the tropical fish in cold water. Disaster! And during the war the place had been an air raid shelter. It seemed a hopeless situation.

Many of the tanks leaked but June added red clay, which settled and went into the holes where it solidified and stopped the leakage. Pleased by this progress, she carried warm water down the stairs from the kitchen in buckets to fill the tanks. Heaters had to be mended and thermostats placed in each tank. It had been a case of simple survival during the war and the aquarium was certainly not on the priority list, frankly it never had been.

June was determined to make a success of the project. She had one book to assist her in understanding tropical fish keeping, 'Life and Love in the Aquarium', published in 1934. Using this single book, her previous knowledge and all her common sense, she set about learning everything she could about this new aspect for the zoo. She loved growing water plants and looking after the fish, over the following years becoming very knowledgeable about running the aquarium.

She often thought about her sister Mew and the last time they had talked. It has been a sad occasion just a few months before the war had ended.

Granny died in 1945, an unhappy event, which brought Mew home for the funeral. Although the two sisters had met from time to time, it was always such a relief to have her big sister home, she harboured a secret desire she would return for good. At the end of the funeral Mew and June had walked in the zoo as they had done so often in the past.

Well, Mew, the war's almost over. What are your plans?"

June almost dreaded asking but thought that she already knew the answer. Mew had left the zoo for a freedom she was not about to relinquish.

"I think you know, June, don't you? You've been in the Land Army. You know how you enjoyed having some life of your own. I have made a decision and I will tell Mum and Dad later today."

"Please don't leave us, Mew. I'd hate that."

June felt desperate. If Mew was leaving then so would she. But in her heart she knew that with the death of granny, to whom Mew was very attached, her sister was finally released from one of the zoo's kinship bondages.

"June, I have to. I want some life of my own. I began to think about it long ago. Remember our walk along the Menai Straits? Well, it was then. I have been accepted as a stewardess on the Cunard liners. I will have the opportunity to visit New Zealand where Uncle Robert's family live."

"Take me with you, Mew. I want to come too".

Mew stopped, turning to face her younger sister, tears welling in her eyes.

"How can you leave Mum? She needs you, June. I am ten years older than you and I must get away now or I never will. I'm proud of Dad, but I am angry with him too. We need some distance between us, and perhaps things will improve then."

Within a week Mew had left. June would write letters to far away places, remembering her sister every day, but Mew had made up her mind to relish the freedom she wanted so much. Now June could only think back to the many happy times she had spent with her sister and just how much she missed her.

So life continued at Chester Zoo. There were no globetrotting choices for the remainder of the family. Molly the elephant was giving rides and proved to be extremely popular. Won Lung the Himalayan bear could still climb out of her pen, as she was very venturesome. Kay often put her back, helped by June. Unfortunately the large bear grew extremely irritable but undeterred, June's mother fearlessly approached her on many occasions, able to lead her back into her pen using titbits of bread.

Unfortunately on one memorable occasion she had decided to go 'walkabout'. Kay jabbed her in her rear end with a pitchfork to turn her around. Lizzie walked up the drive, blissfully unaware that Kay had performed this prickly act of provocation. She wandered up as usual to put her into the pen, having brought some bread covered with honey to tempt her back. She approached Won Lung, holding out the first piece of bread but the bear lunged at her. June's mother vanished under the animal completely! Kay rushed forward with the pitchfork and drove the bear back to the safety of her pen. Elizabeth stood up. June was shaking with shock but her mother made no fuss, walking back to The Oakfield with her daughter.

As they neared the house June suggested that her mother soak in a hot bath, as she knew that she had been bitten. June wanted to send for medical help but Lizzie refused. Ignoring her mother's wishes, June rang the doctor and ran the bath for her mother. June suggested she had a medicinal whiskey but her mother refused. In desperation, June downed the half a tumbler herself!

Lizzie was a very private person, refusing to let even her daughter see where the bear had bitten her. June insisted. There were two round holes where the bear's incisor teeth had sunk into the top of her thigh as well as other bite marks. Each incisor hole was the size of a half crown. The doctor came but there was nothing much that he could do as the holes did not need to be stitched as they weren't bleeding. Lizzie's dress and coat had saved her from more serious injury. She played it all down and the doctor simply left, adding that he'd never had to treat a bear wound before. Lizzie simply redressed and went back to work.

June was still trembling. To this day, though, she remains enormously grateful to Kay. He had saved her mother's life and never received the full credit he deserved.

147

Muriel in the Wrens outside The Oakfield

19

'I can die happy because my polar bears have plenty of room and water'

Miss Tomkyns-Grafton, the lady from Windermere in the Lake District, continued to visit Punch the polar bear. She was a well recognised figure in the zoo and always welcome. Her neat shoes decorated by velvet pom-poms, her slightly old-fashioned clothes and soft voice fascinated June. In her home in the Lake district she bred Clumber spaniels, of which she was very fond.

The villagers from Windermere called her 'The lonely old lady in the big house', but little did they know that her heart lay elsewhere, far to the south in a distant zoo. She cared deeply for Punch the polar bear from the moment she came across him in his cramped pen.

Miss Tomkyns-Grafton led a strict orderly life until one day before the war she read in the newspaper of the gift to Chester Zoo by the late Miss Esther Holt. She decided to visit the zoo, saw Punch and, like June, was fascinated by him, always speaking to him on her twice-yearly visits to Chester. She felt sad about his poor living conditions. She worried, becoming more attached to him as she grew older.

She also gave generously to the birds and other animals. Frequently small parcels of tasty food would arrive at the zoo, special tit bits for the animals and birds. Joining the zoo as an ordinary member she loved to visit. Having 'adopted' Punch and later his companion Judy, the old lady never failed to send a regular cheque for their food. One day as she stood by his pen a little boy came up and as he passed he muttered 'Poor thing.'

Catherine Tomkyns-Grafton made a decision. She approached George Mottershead to enquire about the cost of a swimming pool for Punch, but permission for the pool was not given by the Ministry of Works until almost the end of the war.

When the pool was being constructed she walked into the zoo again. Now over 80 years of age she braved the weather to watch the mechanical diggers moving tons of Cheshire clay for the pool.

The two polar bears were introduced to their new home, both in a very dirty state. Judy was moved first, at 11pm. Early the next morning she plunged into the new pool, swam for an hour and emerged snow white. Punch was caught and transferred around mid-day. He immediately had a long drink then wandered around the new enclosure looking perplexed. At last he plunged into the water, spending a long time swimming and diving, finally cleaning himself. He looked magnificent.

At age eighty three Miss Tomkyns-Grafton travelled to the zoo to see her favourite animal in his new pool. Punch slipped into the deep clean water as if to show his appreciation when she called out. 'Come on boy!' and he delighted her by swimming to and fro across the water. Judy joined him in the 40,000 gallon pool which had cost £300.

Miss Tomkyns-Grafton died suddenly shortly afterwards on November the twenty seventh 1946. George Mottershead received her last cheque for the bears' food the day after her death. It must have been one of the last things she did.

In her will she left the residue of her estate to The North of England Zoological Society.

The message she left for Mr Mott said, "I can die happy because my polar bears have plenty of room and water."

Amazingly the bequest was for £17,838. The Zoo's total reserves were less than £21,500 and the total annual revenue from all other sources was less than £9,000. Finally June had her wish for Punch granted and the legacy was a tremendous help to the zoo, which had struggled so valiantly to survive through the war years.

June was now nineteen years old. Finally she began to realise that her father's vision of a zoo without bars would truly come to fruition during the next decade but at times it was very difficult to see beyond the drudgery of the immediate day-to-day routine.

Once again she was working full time, taking on an enormous amount of work in the absence of her sister Mew. Her mother continued her daily tasks, always caring consistently for both people and animals. Her father was relentlessly ambitious, a fearless ambassador for the zoo, increasing his knowledge almost daily and mixing with wealthy and influential people. She spent very little time talking to him now as the zoo took up all of their time.

An opportunity presented itself one Saturday as the gates closed for the evening. Her father was discussing the ringing in of a wooded area known as the donkey's nest as an enclosure for the wolves. This would provide an extensive area for them to roam in and at the same time the hollowed out ground would deaden their howling which was not at all pleasant.

June wandered over to listen to their conversation and as the keepers left she continued to talk with her father.

"Dad, they are very unreliable, aren't they?"

"Yes, even though they were born here they are completely unpredictable and never to be trusted. They need a lot of watching but this new enclosure will be attractive to the visitors."

He smiled at June as she stood tall and thoughtful by his side, in some ways very like him in character, determined yet quiet, often keeping her thoughts to herself. He missed Muriel but they had rowed over several issues and he sensed that she was not accepting of his behaviour at times. He did not feel that June was so disapproving.

"You've read about Charles Darwin, June? We have discussed his theory of evolution many times and we both agree that it is fundamentally sound. His theory that all species had one common ancestor and as conditions of life changed, so did the living things change and develop."

"It's such an enormous subject, Dad, but I've thought about it over the years, particularly as we are so close to the animals here in the zoo. They are part of our daily life and we can observe them closely."

"Yes, but have you ever thought what we see when we go into the aquarium at the zoo? In times of peace we have been able to collect specimens from all over the world. Then we look at the reptiles. There are thousands of varieties of reptiles in various stages of evolution, but some of the most interesting varieties have long been extinct. Finally there are the birds and animals."

"Yes, but what point are you making, Dad?"

Mr Mott paused, thinking for a minute.

"Well, it is among the birds and animals that the zoo can best exhibit specimens of evolutionary development.... but before that there are the egg-laying mammals which come from Australia. They lay eggs like birds or, to be more correct, like reptiles, and they suckle their young like mammals.

"Think about birds. The different species run into tens of thousands. Then we come to birds that have perfected long distances of flight and eat by scooping up fish from shoals, swallowing them whole. Now imagine June, if pelicans were fed by hand for generations they would eventually lose the power of scooping up great quantities of fish. The large dilatable pouch of the lower mandible would lose its elasticity and after thousands of years we would have a very different bird than the one we have today."

"So you are saying, Dad, that we are part of the evolutionary changes?"

"Of course, June! Take the chimpanzee for example. It has the intelligence of an average child of two to three years of age, and then it seems to stop. But some individual chimps have progressed further than that. It all takes millions of years."

Deep in this engrossing subject the two Mottersheads made their way slowly to The Oakfield. "So you're saying, Dad, that we are evolving too."

"That's right! There is little doubt that millions of years ago, man was no more intelligent than a chimpanzee, and he, like that animal, came from a stock which had its origin in the earliest forms of life."

"So when we look at all the animals in our zoo, everything is part of a wonderful creation? We all fit into an intricate pattern which is steadily moving forward."

"Exactly, June! But remember, many creatures will eventually disappear as prehistoric animals once did. Only their fossil remains will tell the future inhabitants of this world that they ever lived."

June stopped in her tracks. Turning, she looked anxiously at her father. "Dad, could anything stop evolution?"

Her father paused. "Maybe some great catastrophic event may hurl us back thousands of years but let's hope it's not in our lifetimes, June. But the zoo can serve to show the average person how the principle of evolution is being continually perpetrated, if they wish to turn their minds to it."

June paced by her father's side in silence. She realised that she too was an integral part of her father's unique vision. It envisaged something far beyond a zoo without bars and that something was a powerful educational tool for all of those people who quested for knowledge and an understanding beyond their own mortality.

His was a somewhat lonely pioneering journey, one which she now finally understood and appreciated.

The six wolf cubs which had been born at Chester Zoo were now four years old and ready to be moved to the new enclosure surrounded by a five foot wall. Mr Mott had signs made warning the public, and in particular children, not to put hands over the wall or climb on it and in no instance to try and feed the wolves. The only person who could actually approach them was Kay's wife.

The warning signs were painted in red and erected on the trees inside the enclosure. The wolves were highly suspicious of these, suspicious of indeed everything, and sniffed every last stone of their new world until they had scented it and claimed it as their own.

Barriers and wire were also erected until the keepers were satisfied that the animals did not present a danger to anyone. Unfortunately the public, particularly children, flouted the warning signs and insisting on feeding them. Mr Mott was not at the zoo when the first accident occurred. One small boy held out food to a wolf, supported on the wall by his parents and was bitten on his hand. Children dared each other to lean as far as they could over the wall.

Lizzie was horrified, confiding in June that the wolves must be placed in another pen immediately. Unfortunately this did not happen. A few days later disaster struck again. A girl accompanied by two younger boys unfortunately put her hand over the wall to count the wolves. A wolf leapt up, grabbing her hand and tried to pull her into the enclosure. Six people were bitten within a short time.

When Mr Mott arrived back at the zoo, Lizzie was waiting for him.

"People come first. The safety of people must be the most important thing George. I want those wolves placed in another pen immediately or I will leave the zoo."

Her quiet but determined voice left her husband in no doubt. He made the decision to shoot all six of them. He did not have sufficient staff to safeguard the enclosure and there were no other safer pens available. No more risks could be taken. It was a very serious matter and had been reported heavily and harshly in the press. He must be seen to be doing the responsible thing.

Much family discussion followed but June had little to say. She revealed her thoughts in a poem which was published in 'Our Zoo News'.

To the Wolves

Most truculent of creatures
As they ran all wild and free,
Across and up the bankings
And round and round the trees.

For them it was but nature
To attack the human race,
To fight to kill and conquer
Was to them the finest grace.

They followed but their instinct,
These hated of all beasts;
They did not know the horror
That on others they released.

So let us, when we think of them,
Remember that we too
Have instincts like all animals,
That is not all so true.

Then let us all forgive them,
For to them it was a game;
And maybe in return for that
They will do for us the same.

Won Lung

The drive to the new bear pits which Miss Tompkins
Grafton helped to pay for. The concrete roads blocks used
in WW 2 were utilised to form the edge of the drive

Punch and Judy in their new enclosure

Fred Williams as a keeper feeding the sea lions

20

Christy

In 1945 an orphaned lion cub entered June Mottershead's life. She named her Christy and the relationship between the two was unique. Lovely lasting memories of the cub would remain with June for the rest of her life.

Christy lost her mother when the next cub to be born was in a breech position and could not be saved. It died along with the mother leaving Christy with only one chance for survival, to be hand reared. The female cub was given to June and the pair became inseparable. Night and day June cared for her, bottle feeding her like a human baby until she grew fat and healthy.

She grew up in The Oakfield, as she was so good natured, becoming part of the Mottershead family. By seven weeks she weighed 12 pounds and June declared that she was the sweetest best-tempered lion cub she had ever known.

She followed June about like a dog, grew quickly and by eleven weeks she turned the scales at 19 pounds. She became quite bossy, showing her mother's temper but never with June. She was given two bottles of milk as soon as she woke up each morning. One day when ready for her next meal she pounced on George Mottershead's bald head as he was leaning forward tying his shoe laces!

Once Christy had eaten she would lie back in June's arms just like a human child and go to sleep. After a nap she awoke and wanted to play with all the family. She bounded round to each one of them wanting a playful companion but if no one responded she attacked the furniture! Immediately everyone had to join in her games until she was exhausted, tired and hungry. Once again she attacked the furniture, cutting her teeth on the back of the dining chairs and sharpening her claws on anything solid. There was not enough time in the day to play with her; she was so full of mischief and energy. When she was shown her sleeping blanket she would trot to June's room and sleep all night. Sometimes she even carried her own blanket up the stairs of The Oakfield. June was so proud of her swift progress.

As the weather improved Christy was taken for walks following behind June and her mother like a dog. She met Peter the Sealyham but although slightly interested, she wasn't allowed to stay with him. Peter had been used to a fully-grown lion as a companion! June introduced her, from a distance, to her father Patrick, grandparents and aunts but she was very nervous, not really ready to associate herself with them.

Christy now weighed in at thirty pounds and when she pounced on June's back, the two of them crashed to the floor. She loved to walk in front of June and then trip her with her front paw. As she followed June she would creep up, hooking her paw round June's ankle, trying again to bring her to the ground. Within a few weeks she had ripped George's best overcoat to shreds, appeared in the kitchen covered in feathers and down, and virtually dissected June's bed. Mr Mott had to make a decision: she must fully enter the life of a zoo animal. Remembering Mowgli, however, the family decided to wean Christy off her human family in slow stages.

June made her a bed in a curtained-off part of the kitchen where she was very comfortable and waited each morning for her feed. Unfortunately one morning she attacked a bag of whitening, dragging it from a cupboard. The tablecloth was ripped to shreds and Christy had a curiously satisfied look in her eyes.

So now it was out of doors for the young lioness, or there would be no home left! The entire family missed her company in the evenings, each one of them in turn sneaking off to check her in the pen she had been contained in. It felt like leaving a baby of four months outside and somehow it didn't seem right.

When June came to release her each morning she tumbled out, so happy to be free again. For two hours she had the entire freedom of the zoo before visitors arrived but then she had to be locked in her pen in the courtyard until the evening. Then once more June allowed her out until dark. She was only a playful creature but could be very rough.

Each evening she accompanied June and her Mum on the nightly walk as they fed tit bits to the animals. Christy would often approach them and give occasional licks through the wire. June wondered how long this could continue as she watched Christy chasing the pea fowl and rabbits. It only needed one kill to change everything but she knew that her father was hoping for the day when the open-air lion enclosure would be completed so that Christy could have a large area to roam in.

Christy was now a very heavy young lioness and June loved her so much. Out on walks, Christy's favourite pastime was to stealthily creep up to the back of June and spring up, grabbing her by the hips whereupon June would slowly sink to the ground with the lioness's solid weight. It was all good harmless fun.

Elizabeth and her daughter had many happy walks through the zoo grounds, each marvelling at Christy's growth and massive strength. She was so gentle; never a claw or bared teeth were displayed. There was total trust between animal and human.

Finally the dreaded words came, "No more letting her loose! She's almost fully grown and she could turn dangerous."

Once her father had left the zoo grounds in the evening, which was often, June and her mum defied him, letting Christy out when all the visitors had gone. They had wonderful times with her but the trouble was she did not want to go back into her cage so she would lie down and refuse to move! Then June and her mother decided that they would carry, or rather drag, her in. June took her two front legs and her mother the two back legs and they would laughingly drag her towards her cage. Christy knew exactly what they were doing and lay prone in a heavy lump making it very difficult for them. Never once did she show her teeth or her claws.

One night Mr Mott came back early and discovered what they were doing. The firm order went out. The zoo could not afford to have an accident or any kind of incidents. If visitors found out that a lioness was roaming freely in the grounds imagine what would happen? There would be a public outcry.

"It's time. She must go in with the other lions."

That was Mr Mott's decision but it certainly wasn't Christy's . She snarled and backed away from her kind, refusing to go near to them or to enter the sleeping quarters. She remained in the outside pen. She would lie against the side of the wire which was closest to her late home, and pine.

Some of the keepers could go in to her, but not Kay. Maybe she could scent elephant on him and on one occasion she chased him. He only avoided being mauled by throwing his coat over her face and using the seconds it gave him to scramble out of the gate.

Without consulting June, Mr Mott arranged for Christy to leave the zoo along with a male lion. Sadly Punch the polar bear finally died in 1946, aged forty two years of age, and a new polar bear was negotiated for the zoo in exchange for the two lions. The zoo was changing rapidly.

June grieved for many years over the fate of Christy. Even though she was 20 years old, this separation was more painful than any other. She felt she had betrayed Christy's trust. How could such a wonderful and gentle creature ever trust humans again? June, not for the first time, certainly didn't feel inclined to.

June honoured her unique friendship with Christy the lioness. She kept her promise, never becoming attached to any animal she didn't own. If June had had her way she would have kept her beloved Christy at the zoo forever.

Mr and Mrs Mottershead hand rearing Christy in The Oakfield

Christy the cub

Christy and June in the kitchen garden

Christy the adult lioness

21

'For June was never to leave her Zoo'

Two thousand visitors came to the zoo on Whit Monday of 1947; the record for a single day. Queues stretched along the pathways and into the buildings. Lines of enthusiastic visitors waited at the entrance. Crowds lined up patiently for the cafés and many people stood impatiently waiting outside the toilets.

There were inadequate facilities for such a large influx of visitors as the main priority of the zoo had been to build safer and more appropriate housing for the animals. June watched as the new cafeteria was built in haste using scrap aluminium sheets bought from the aircraft factory at Broughton. Redundant iron window frames from Williams & Williams, a nearby factory, were speedily incorporated into the new café. She remembered her brief time spent working there helping to make jerry cans during the war. She had hated entering this factory and now part of it had come to the zoo! June continued her work, which she had begun in 1946, in the extended aquarium in the cellar which had been closed during the war.

New toilets were hastily erected, poorly done with cheap materials they served their purpose until more adequate ones were built. As this was happening Sammy and Susie the sea lions arrived at the zoo and they were put in the polar bear pool, as the pool for sea lions was incomplete. As workers struggled to dig down as deeply as 12 feet into the hard Cheshire clay, the polar bears had to be kept in dens and the brown bears were left outside in their pen.

Everywhere there was building activity. Ex-army roadblocks were put into place around the new pool and chestnut fencing was erected on top of them to keep the sea lions in. Chestnut fencing was often used at this time for keeping the animals inside their enclosures, but it wasn't very successful.

Water was needed to fill the pool so Mr Mott sank a borehole at the far end. After it had run through the sea lion pool, it was channelled to another field which was now being developed.

This canal was extended into yet another field and an island of mud was deliberately made and planted with fast growing willows and a few slower growing trees including a cedar tree. Mr Mott had no boat but, ever practical, decided to put a plank of wood across the inner tube of a large aircraft tyre which he had picked up at a war surplus sale. It was almost impossible to steer and difficult to reach the island.

Determined he would not to be beaten Mr Mott secured a rope between the bank and the island so that the family could pull the makeshift 'boat' across. Watched by the family he climbed 'aboard' to sail to the island but the contraption moved so slowly that he gave a big tug on the rope. To everyone's horror the tyre shot from beneath him! He dangled above the muddy water on the rope for a few seconds and then slowly sank! Everyone burst out laughing. It reminded June of the similar incident long ago when she was a small girl. Granny had slipped into the duck pond and sank beneath the mud in much the same way as her son had done.

Finally a rowing boat was bought and visitors took sixpenny trips round the island.

The outdoor lion enclosure was finally completed. Built of wire mesh fencing and the plentiful supply of roadblocks, it became most probably the first time that lions had ever been kept behind wire. All other zoos used strong iron bars for their cages. Her father's dream of a zoo without bars was becoming a reality.

Miss Bully from Ness had paid £600 for the wire. Planning had started 9 years earlier but now it was finally completed. Opened by a radio personality, Norman Ellison, it attracted huge attention making the zoo even more popular.

Now attention was given to the drives in the extended part of the zoo. Red shale was laid as it was cheap but everyone complained, as it was almost impossible to brush. Litter became a problem as every piece had to be picked up by hand. As soon as more money was available cinders were laid over the shale but still it was no adequate answer.

Everyone was delighted when finally the drives were sealed and brushing could take place.

The war years had taken a huge toll on the zoo but little by little it began to change. June was satisfied that finally it was no longer such a struggle to maintain and also build and modernise within the grounds. The sea lions, polar and brown bears all had enclosures. Walking around the zoo was a pleasure and she proudly showed all the changes to Mew when she returned on a home visit.

June's twenty-first birthday arrived but it was spent serving an evening meal to a party of old age pensioners in The Oakfield Café. Already hating any café work, she was not happy to celebrate her birthday in this way but there was no one else to do the work. Twenty-one-year old June had no choices. She wasn't given one, as it was an expectation that she should help out as always, even on top of a full day's work.

Grimly she served the teas, wondering to herself if life would ever be any different in years to come.

After helping with the teas she rushed over to check some parakeets which were breeding really well and then on to the aquarium where a British adder had given birth to live young. At first she had thought that they were worms but on closer inspection she realised that they were young snakes, and they took a very long time to gather up.

Living with mum and dad and having them as her bosses on the job meant that she could always be called upon whenever and wherever needed. As she could do virtually any work in the zoo the need for her help was daily and constant.

Service men who had been demobbed worked at the zoo. Ziggy, a Pole, an Italian, and a boy from Nepal who was waiting for a boat to sail home on, all provided some interesting conversations for June. Charlie Collins who had left the zoo to do war work finally returned in 1948 much to June's delight. His work at the Ministry of Defence had come to an end but for a while he stayed in the south of the country, driving taxis. Whenever he was passing the zoo he called in for it was, after all, the nearest thing to a real home he had ever had. At last the need to return there became too great, and he was warmly welcomed back remaining at the zoo for the rest of his working life. Here he would marry and have children.

Upon his initial return he began working with his 'sister' once again, and June's mood lifted. June had of course always considered him to be her brother. Together they commented on the huge changes in the ever-expanding zoo. More animals arrived, more people arrived and finally the balance sheet for the end of April showed a net profit of £1,439/19/1d

Charlie Collins proved to be a steadfast colleague and friend to June. During 1948 the workload steadily increased to a point where June felt she could not manage the newly built reptile house on top of her other jobs. She started refusing to look after it. Charlie gradually took on that job and many others.

June grew a wide variety of plants in the snake pens in the aquarium and the new reptile cases were built for vegetation to grow in. Charlie loved plants as much as June and they became his top priority in the new house. A green mamba lived in there. Sinuous silent and lethal, he would appear to drape himself innocently along branches watching every move. Charlie often tried to trap him before entering to tend to his plants, but many times he would weigh up the situation and take a risk. If the mamba was lying along a branch far away from the door, Charlie would enter. June knew how angry her Dad would have been had he known how Charlie diced with the mamba, but it was their secret and anyway Charlie knew his reptiles and never took too many risks.

Everything he looked after, whether it was vegetation or animals, thrived. He succeeded in keeping a Mella's chameleon for over two years, which was a record. Finally June had an enormous amount of work simply looking after the fish and breeding parakeets so Charlie trained Roger, one of the other keepers, to help him with his duties.

Charlie was an incredibly versatile builder and gifted at working with sandstone. When he completed buildings he told June that they would still be standing long after he had gone. In 1948 a new reptile house had to be built in a great hurry as George Cansdale the zoologist had sent a consignment of snakes from West Africa. These new arrivals made the old cellar alongside the aquarium totally inadequate. For a while they were kept in the bathroom of The Oakfield! Charlie and Mrs Maddox built the new reptile house mainly on their own from scrap materials such as the ubiquitous roadblocks (used for the foundations), iron from scrap yards, timber from a disused poultry house, and armour plated glass from Pilkington's glass manufacturers at St. Helen. The only new material was Perspex sheeting for the roof.

It was no coincidence that Charlie was entrusted to drive the only van which the zoo owned. He was a member of the family. Mrs Maddox worked in the café but when they were not busy she helped Charlie with the building. Most of the staff gave up their free time to do jobs around the zoo such as helping in the café, manning the pay boxes, picking up litter and helping to mend fences. During the war years it had been mere survival but now the staff were almost bubbling with optimism for the zoo's future, feeling that considerable progress was really being made.

Someone else had entered June's hard working life in 1947 but at the time she didn't realised how important their first meeting was. Many service men were demobbed and working at the zoo, amongst them a young man with a lovely smile. June liked him instantly. Initially she spotted him with a crowd of workers, admiring him from a distance. She quietly appreciated his fit body, tanned skin and laughing eyes, noting how well he related to other workers. Fred Williams had been under training for aircrew as a wireless operator mechanic in the RAF. He loved animals and that is why he came to the zoo. He had volunteered for the duration of the war and was able to get demobbed. It soon became apparent that Fred had a talent for planning and building, a skill, which did not go unnoticed by June's father.

To her delight the young man was sent down to the aquarium house to help June. They worked side by side with little to say. June was shy but very attracted towards him. He had an easy pleasant manner, which set her at ease. She began to tell him about her zoo and he was fascinated.

"You've been here since you were 4 years old! I can hardly believe that."

Fascinated by the girl with hidden depths and strengths who kept her distance despite their effortless chatting, he looked forward to the days when they could work together. Her bright and versatile mind intrigued him. Other women simply did not match up to her. June Mottershead was very different.

"You were asking me what I'd done in the war years. Well, I trained for air crew as a wireless operator, I haven't been long out of the air force.."

As he talked June was weighing him up as she did with all people. He was steady and reliable she decided. In some ways he reminded her of her dad, he was eminently practical.

She casually mentioned him to her mum who had already noticed what a good worker he was, but no one suspected what was about to happen.

One evening Fred and June decided to collect sticklebacks for the aquarium. Armed with nets and wearing their old clothes and boots they eagerly set off to the pond. Yet this time it was different. There was a meaningful but loaded silence between them. Neither one wished to break it.

As they scooped out the creatures and separated them from the weed the young man turned to June and gently took the net from her hand, laying it on the bank. She stared at him in silence but in touching trust. Gently he lifted her head up and they stared into each other's eyes. Then he leaned over and kissed her gently on the lips.

For weeks theirs was a growing silent affection. No one knew the significance when they went off to the cinema or to ice-skating with Fred's sister and her boyfriend. No one knew about the love they bore for each other for Fred understood how private June was, private and very special.

His love for her showed itself in the strangest of ways, not always successfully. Inspired by the work with the fish, he built a small aquarium on top of the family piano in his mother's home and it ruined the wood! He always arrived at work in the zoo before everyone else to catch up with June in private and his happiness was evident. Not until they announced that they were to be engaged in 1948 did anyone of the family know, except maybe Charlie and he was not about to tell.

Finally and somewhat nervously Fred Williams asked Mr Mott for June's hand in marriage. "This is the most fightening thing I've ever done," he told June with relief in his voice, but Mr and Mrs Mott were delighted at the prospect of Fred becoming their son in law. Mr Mott shook his hand, happily giving his consent to their marriage.

June had found her mate for life. Their marriage took place on the twenty sixth of February 1949. He remains with her to this present day, approaching almost sixty happy years together years of togetherness. Fred immersed himself fully into the Mottershead family dream of 'The zoo without bars', working there for many years alongside his wife.

For June was never to leave her zoo. What had started as a childhood dream, a journey into an unknown garden, which slowly evolved into the vision which her father dreamed of, became June's destiny.

Despite the many times when she had questioned her father, regardless of the loss of her childhood, sacrificed to hard work, family loyalty and commitment she was absorbed into the life which sprang from her father's passion; a zoological garden where people could observe and learn about animals without looking through iron bars and seeing them as imprisoned creatures.

Yet when June walks about the zoo in her eighties, she remembers with great clarity and empathy those years between 1930 and 1948 when the zoo was born and grew, witnessed by an articulate and sensitive girl who was so very instrumental in its development.

She pauses, looking at The Oakfield from the distance of the lawns, and remembering Minnie the tapir carrying her on rides which took her to the walled garden. She retraces the pathways to the now gardened area where Punch spent his life; she hears the roar of Mowgli and the bark of his little companion Peter; sees Mollie and Kay swaying in unison as the great elephant makes her way to the orchard. She sees her mother calling her from the front step of the great red house; Mew hurrying to feed the chimps, her long black coat wrapped tightly around her to protect her against the cold winds of winter; the smoke rising from the Lodge as granny does her house work and the spiral of smoke from the garden as grandad digs and nurtures the earth. She sees her father rushing off, accompanied by a keeper, yet again investigating the whereabouts of Ferdinand the bison.

She sees the bushes part as her most beloved Christy comes bounding out to meet her.

This is June's zoo.

June taking Christy for a walk

June and Fred's wedding at the Oakfield on the 26th of February 1949